SAINT HUBERT

SAINT BRIDGET

SAINT GILES   SAINT FRANCIS

SAINT DOROTHEA

TEN SAINTS

By ELEANOR FARJEON

With Illustrations By
HELEN SEWELL

HENRY Z. WALCK, INC.
NEW YORK

CONTENTS

SAINT CHRISTOPHER   *Third Century*   9

SAINT MARTIN   *Fourth Century*   16

SAINT DOROTHEA   *Fourth Century*   31

SAINT BRIDGET   *Fifth Century*   35

SAINT PATRICK   *Fifth Century*   45

SAINT HUBERT   *Seventh Century*   63

SAINT GILES   *Sixth Century*   74

SAINT SIMEON STYLITES   *Fifth Century*   77

SAINT NICHOLAS   *Fourth Century*   89

SAINT FRANCIS   *Thirteenth Century*   99

TEN SAINTS

· SAINT CHRISTOPHER ·

TWO HUNDRED YEARS after the birth of Christ there was a man in Samos who had not heard of him. This man had the stature of a giant. If the mightiest tree in the forest had come to life, it would have resembled him. No weight was too heavy for his arms to lift or his back to bear, nothing that needed strength was too hard for him to do. His ways were rude, his mind was ignorant. His eyes were the eyes of a dog. They glowed under his shaggy hair with the look of one that longs to serve a beloved master. This giant was stronger than any man he knew, and in his simplicity had no other test. Whom then could he serve and adore? His child's heart urged him to go in search of the strongest king in the world. Taking his staff, he went alone to find him.

On the road he stopped one and another to ask who was the mighti est king. Each gave him the same answer: "Pharaoh, who else, you dog?" The giant then asked where Pharaoh was to be found, and came at last to the city as a dog to its kennel.

People looked amazed at the strange figure. "The dog-headed man! The dog-headed man!" cried the children, scampering from him. Yet he meant no man harm, and least of all the young ones. Rumour ran through the streets that a giant with a dog's head was come among them, and when he reached the palace, Pharaoh himself was standing there in his golden splendour. If he smiled to see how this huge stran-ger, with his matted locks, blunt features, and melting eyes, had been mistaken for a dog, the king also marvelled at his size and strength.

"Who are you, stranger?" asked Pharaoh.

The giant gazed at him as though he himself did not know who he was, and was still waiting to be told. Instead of answering, he shook his shaggy mane and said: "Are you the mighty Pharaoh?"

"I am he."

Then the giant lay down at his feet on the palace steps, and said: "Be my master." Pharaoh nodded, and the giant made ready to love him.

In the next days, the giant followed the king wherever he went; and Pharaoh was well-pleased with his new servant, for no other could boast of one so big and willing. One day as they passed through the city they heard two men quarrelling; one cursed the other, and wished the Prince of Darkness might fly away with him. Instantly Pharaoh shrank and crossed himself.

"Why do you do that?" asked the giant.

"It is well to do so whenever that name is said."

"The name of the Prince of Darkness?"

"Be silent!" Pharaoh blenched, and crossed himself again.

"Farewell, O King!" said the giant.

"Where are you going?"

"To find the King you fear, who is stronger than you." And the giant strode out of the city, with grief in his eyes.

Now he stopped each he met, to ask where the Prince of Darkness dwelt, and each turned and ran from him with a horror he could not understand. But he had no need to ask often, for that Prince lies in wait for those who look for him. On a lonely road he appeared in his black splendour, and the simple giant said: "Are you the Prince of Darkness?"

"I am he."

Then the giant lay down in the dust, saying: "Be my master."

The Dark Prince beckoned, and the giant prepared to love him. He followed the Prince along a lonely way, wondering how he would be required to serve him. Anon he saw his new master stop and shrink. "We must go another road," he muttered hoarsely.

"Why must we do that?"

"Because of this." The Prince of Darkness pointed to a simple wooden Cross set up by the wayside. The giant went up to it, and saw there nothing to fear, only the figure of a poor naked Man.

"How can this hurt you?" said the wondering giant. But the Prince of Darkness dwindled under his eyes, and even as he gazed, was there no more.

Then the giant saw that the Figure on the Cross was wearing a crown. He thought: "If this One is stronger than the one who is gone, He is the King I must serve." And he went in search of God, and did not know it.

SAINT CHRISTOPHER

After a while he came to a broad river, running swift and strong between its banks. On the far side a brown-robed hermit knelt outside a cabin. This was the first man the giant had seen for a day, so he stepped into the river, making nothing of it, and strode to the other bank. The hermit, having ended his prayer, watched the giant coming, and when the shaggy fellow stood on dry ground, shaking the water off his feet and legs, the holy man asked: "What has brought you here?"

"I seek a stronger King than the Prince of Darkness."

"Whom do you mean?"

"I do not know," said the giant. His eyes fell on the Cross the hermit had prayed to, and pointing to it he said: "That is the Man."

The hermit told him: "It is Christ the Redeemer of the world you seek."

"How can I find and serve Him?" asked the giant.

"He can be found and served with prayer," said the hermit. "Kneel down and pray."

The giant shook his head. "I cannot. I do not know how."

The hermit saw that he could not yet make the giant understand the nature of prayer. It would be like trying to speak to a dog, or an infant. Yet those melting eyes seemed to be asking his help.

"If you do not know how to pray now, you shall learn one day. Stay here meanwhile. There is work for a ferryman. The current is strong, and travellers who come to the ford must sometimes turn back."

"None need do so more," said the giant joyfully. "I will carry all comers over on my shoulders." If the current was strong, he knew himself to be stronger, and his back able to bear anything laid upon it.

So there he dwelt and passed his days, now being on one bank, now on the other. Nothing that had to be carried was too heavy for him. He bore men with their packs, and women with their baskets; rich men and poor, armies on horseback, merchants with their camels, peasants with their households. He took their children two on either shoulder, and when he had carried the people, he carried their goods. Even their asses and oxen, their horses and carts, he carried over the ford without thinking twice. A man was no more to him than a sack of meal, or a girl than a bunch of flowers. The work made him happy, because his strength was of service; yet also sad because, serving all, he did not seem to serve One.

One night when he was making ready to sleep, thinking no traveller likely to come so late, he heard a small clear voice call: "Ferryman!"

He went down to the ford, and there stood a Child. The giant had never seen one so light and so little, standing alone on its feet. He asked: "What is it you want, Child?"

"I want to go over the river, ferryman."

"Is nobody with you, Child?"

"I am alone. How shall I get to the other side, ferryman?"

"I will carry you on my back, Child."

"Shall I not be too heavy for you, ferryman?"

The giant picked up that fragile Child as though he had been a feather, and set him on his back. Then, taking his staff, he stepped into the dark water, scarce knowing he bore any burden at all.

He had not waded a quarter of the distance when he said: "Child, you weigh more than I thought." He was surprised to feel his shoulders begin to ache. Half-way across he wiped his streaming brow. "Child, is it you who are heavy, or I who am weak? I never carried so great a burden before." He staggered forward, straining on his staff. Three parts of the way over he halted and groaned. "Child, I feel as though I had the world on my shoulders." He thought his back must break before he could reach the bank. That last part of the way seemed longer than all the rest, each step cost the giant so dear. At last he stumbled on dry ground, and lifted the Child off gently. Then, being exhausted, he lay down in the grass.

He heard the Child say: "Christopher! thou hast borne the world on thy shoulders. I created the world, I redeemed the world, I bear the sins of the world."

When Christopher looked up, the Child had vanished. But he knew Who it was had given him his name, he knew Who it was he had carried over the river. Putting his lips to the place where the Child had stood, he whispered: "Be my Master."

A RHYME FOR CHRISTOPHER

(July 25th)

"Carry me, Ferryman, over the ford."
"My boat is my back, little boy. Come aboard.
Some men have muscle, and some men have mind,
And my strength is my gift for the good of mankind."

"Shall I not weigh on you crossing the ford?"
"I've carried a king with his crown and his sword,
A labourer too with his spade and his plough.
What's a mere child to me? Come along now."

"Ferryman, why do you pant in the ford?"
"My muscles are iron, my sinews are cord,
But my back with your burden is ready to break,
You double your weight, child, with each step I take!"

"Ferryman, bearer of men o'er the ford,
Christopher, Christopher, I am your Lord.
My frame may be little, and slender my girth,
But they hold all the sorrows and sins of the earth.

"You have borne the whole world on your back through the ford,
You have carried a King with His crown and His sword,
A Labourer too with His spade and His plough,
And in one Child all little ones. Put me down now."

Christopher set the Child down on the sward.
Christopher fell on his face by the ford.
He heard a voice uttering: "Keep Me in mind!
Our strength is our gift for the good of mankind."

• SAINT MARTIN •

THE Roman Legions of the Emperor Constantius had come to Sabaria, a town in the land we now call Hungary. But in those days it was called Pannonia. A native of the town presented himself to one of the Roman Tribunes, and said he wished to enrol his son in the army.

"We are always glad of likely soldiers," said the Tribune. "There's plenty to do in Gaul. How old is this son of yours?"

"Fifteen," said the man of Sabaria.

"What is his name?"

"Martin."

"And he is eager to become a soldier, you say?"

"I say nothing of the sort. He wants to become a monk. Did you ever hear of such a life for a man?"

The Tribune laughed. "There are Christians enough among our legionaries, but they all prefer the helmet to the cowl. I suppose your lad is a Christian?"

"No," said Martin's father. "That new religion finds no favour here. Isn't our old faith good enough for the boy? Haven't we Arian Bishops of our own? Yet if you'll believe me, he is for ever arguing on points of doctrine, as though he knew better than they do! — a boy like him!"

"Let me see this boy," said the Tribune, thinking no doubt that any youth who wished to be a monk instead of a soldier must be a weedy weakling. But when Martin was brought before him he changed his opinion. The young Sabarian was tall and gallant, and his eyes were as keen as they were thoughtful.

"He has the makings of a soldier in him," said the Tribune; and against his will, Martin was enrolled. When the Romans left Pannonia for Gaul, he said farewell to his parents and went with them. His father was glad to see him go. His mother wept.

Young Martin made the best of his soldiering. He found something good in the stern discipline of his training. The exercises and the strict self-control appealed to him; and his strong sense of duty made him obedient. But he hated much that went with a soldier's life, and above all the violence of warfare. During his first three years, if anyone asked: "Who is that fine young fellow over there?" his comrades laughed and replied: "He? He is Martin of Pannonia, the mildest soldier that ever drew a sword!" Yet none of his comrades dreamed of calling this mild Martin a coward. He rode his horse and used his sword as well as the best of them. He was more rigorous with himself than they. He lived sparingly, where his comrades indulged themselves. He never took his ease after a battle, and its rewards were nothing to him; he wanted neither loot, nor fortune, nor a high command. In spite of this, because he could control both himself and men, at the end of three years Martin was made a Tribune.

Constantius the Emperor was a Christian; but the Caesar of the Roman Army was the Emperor's cousin Julian. Men called him the Apostate, because from childhood he had turned his back on Christ. It was Julian who led the Romans into Gaul, and made Paris his city. Martin was among the troops he commanded, and in the course of keeping order in the country was sent here and there.

One day the young Tribune found himself outside the gates of Amiens. He rode a fine horse, and over his armour wore a rich red cloak. The foot-soldiers were passing through the city-gates. Beside it crouched a naked beggar with his bowl. The day was cold, and he shivered as he prayed for charity. But none listened to him, or if they did, it was only to fling him a scornful glance, a rough word, or thrust him off with their feet. Beggars were as common as mongrels, one could not be bothered with them.

"Charity for the hungry! pity the cold!" pleaded the beggar.

"Come, Marcus, best foot foremost!" shouted a soldier. "I'm perished! There are good inns in Ambianum for meat and drink and fire."

"In Christ's name!" sighed the beggar. But the soldiers were not thinking about Christ. They mocked at him, and passed by.

When the footmen had gone through the gate, Martin came riding up on his horse. Did the beggar say anything more? Or did he only hug his empty bowl to his bare body, and shiver? Their eyes met.

Martin, as it happened, had nothing to give. He drew his sword, cut his cloak in two, and let one-half fall on the beggar's nakedness.

That night, stretched on his pallet, the young Tribune had a dream. He beheld Christ seated in heaven, wearing the half-mantle. Did his eyes appear to Martin's like those of the poor beggar at the gate? Did a voice like the beggar's say in his dark tent: "Inasmuch as ye have done it unto one of the least of these, ye have done it unto Me"?

When he awoke in the morning, his dream was still on him. He had not yet been baptized; now he delayed no longer. He went straightway and was received into the church of Christ. How gladly he would have changed, at the same time, his hard life in a soldier's tent for one still harder in a hermit's cell. But the life he was destined for was not yet to be, and for two years more Martin remained a soldier.

It was the year three-hundred-and-fifty-eight. Julian the Apostate marched his troops to the frontier of Gaul. The barbarous tribes of the Allemanni were threatening it. While Julian held the line in Gaul, Romans poured over the Alps from Italy, and the Allemanni were between two fires. Martin spent twenty-four months of bitter struggle in Julian's camp. He obeyed the Caesar's military orders, and issued his own orders to his men; but while his body submitted to the world, his heart and soul turned more and more to God. One fierce battle followed another, and he was filled with increasing horror of the things demanded of him as a soldier. At last the crisis in his spirit was reached, and he presented himself in Julian's tent.

The Apostate was busy with his plans. He was on the eve of a campaign which meant success or defeat. He supposed the young Tribune had come upon some military matter.

"Well, Martin, what is it?"

"Caesar," said Martin, "I wish to be released."

Julian looked at him, not understanding such an incredible request at such a time. "Released from what?"

"From military service."

Too amazed to be angry, Julian exclaimed: "You ask to terminate your life as a soldier?"

"Yes, Caesar."

"I refuse to do it, coward!" said Julian with contempt.

Martin met his scornful eye without shame. "Caesar," he said, "put me in the forefront of the army, and take away from me my breast-plate and sword. I will go into the battle ahead of my comrades, but I will not for any man, caesar, or emperor, draw sword and take life again."

"You are mad," said Julian.

"Was Christ?" asked Martin. "I am His soldier."

"You are the soldier of the Emperor Constantius." Julian summoned an officer and pointed to Martin. "Put this man in irons. After the battle I will deal with him."

Martin was taken from the tent, and chained. Julian, frowning, returned to his plans. He had believed in this man — and perhaps, against his will, believed in him still. But he had darkened his understanding against Christ. He saw nothing for it but death for a Roman soldier who refused to fight, yet agreed to die.

Before the battle was fought, a little body of men came to the Roman camp, from the camp of the Allemanni. They were a deputation, asking for peace. Julian named his terms, and they were accepted. The battle Martin had refused was never fought.

Julian had nobility in his nature. He seized the occasion to have Martin's chains struck off. Perhaps he honoured the young Tribune too much to risk a refusal twice. He sent for him.

"There is peace for awhile," he said, "and since you no longer wish to lead the life of a soldier, you may depart."

Martin went out of his tent to follow Christ, while the Apostate remained to strive against Him.

* * *

Martin was still no more than twenty years old when he went south to Poitiers, and became the disciple of the Bishop Hilary. He had no need to put away worldly desires, for he had never had any. His humblest wish was for a life of self-denial, now in seclusion in the monastery, now going on Christ's business among men. He was always happiest when in retirement; and when Hilary wished to make him a deacon of the Church, he said it was too great an honour for him.

But Hilary knew that Martin had special gifts. "Some office you must hold," he told the young monk.

"Then let me be Exorcist, and battle with the devil."

"You could not have chosen a harder office," said Hilary. "The priest who has to exorcise the devil must prepare himself for the devil's abuse and insult, and even perhaps for his whip."

"That is why I choose it," answered Martin. And he set himself to his life-long task of fighting evil wherever he saw it.

Soon after this, he asked to be sent to Pannonia. He had a longing to save men's souls in his native land. It was no easy journey; he travelled afoot through wild alpine passes, where robbers lurked. A band of thieves fell on him in a lonely pass; monk and merchant were all one to them, and they plundered Martin of the little he had on him. But while they did so he spoke such words of grace that they went off with his silver in their pouches and his gold in their ears. The silver was soon spent; but presently one of the thieves found the gold a wealth he could not squander. He left his way of life, and became a peaceable citizen, and Martin never knew it. He would have held his silver cheap at such a price.

And now he was come again to Sabaria, where to his joy his Mother was still living. She had closed her door on a boy in a shining casque, she opened it on a man in a brown cowl.

The boy and the man were equally dear to her; she was ready to love and eager to listen to him. She was her son's first convert. Soon others followed her. Martin found that the priests in Pannonia were still preaching the old Arian Creed, which as a boy he had been unable to accept. His spirit was roused; there was something of the soldier in him still, and Christ's battles were never fought with a tongue more eloquent, a presence more irresistible, than Martin's. His face was alight with fervour and serenity, the power of the spirit streamed from him when he spoke. Faith in God and pity for men were one in him. Wherever Martin saw a fellow in misery, he saw his Redeemer wearing the Crown of Thorns.

But the Arian Bishops were alarmed by his successes, and angered by his protests; and among those who would not give ear to him was his father.

"Hold your peace, boy!" said the man of Sabaria, "if you don't want to get yourself into trouble."

Warnings of that sort meant less than nothing to Martin.

"Woman!" said the father to the mother, "do you know they are threatening to beat our son in the market-place? He is your child—make him hold his tongue."

Martin's tongue, set on speaking the truth, spoke on.

At last his father's fears were realized; the Arian Bishops had him whipped, and driven out of Pannonia. He was, after all, only a poor young priest, and they were powerful princes of their church. When Martin took his last leave of his mother—

"Go back to Poitiers and the good Hilary," she whispered. But Martin shook his head.

"No, Mother. I hear Hilary has been treated as I have been; the Arians have expelled him from his See. I shall go over the mountains into Italy."

"Are there no Arians there?"

"There are Arians everywhere."

"Then you'll be beaten again!"

"And again and again, if need be!" As if it mattered to Martin. He journeyed over the Alps into Milan, knowing he had left a light to shine behind him.

In Milan the tale of Sabaria was repeated. Vehemently and defiantly Martin preached Christ, and was driven out of the city. He went on again, like a pioneer blazing his trail through a dark forest, leaving his words in the ears of men and women who remembered them; and came at last to rest for awhile in the lovely little Isle of Gallinaria. It was a white isle, floating like a pearl on a sapphire sea.

Here for a time Martin found peace in solitude; he fed his body on roots, and his mind on meditation. Yet even his sunny haven had its dangers. Martin found slopes of beautiful pale green flowers set amid dark green leaves, and in his ignorance he ate of them. Strong spasms of pain took him when he had eaten a little, and he all but died. The pain came quick enough to save his life, for the plant was the deadly hellebore, and if he had eaten more he must have died. But after this his days on Gallinaria were untroubled. This was the one long season of rest he knew, and he loved his white isle on the deep blue sea, under the shadow of high silent mountains. Then word was borne to him that Bishop Hilary had returned to Poitiers, and Martin said farewell to idleness. The time to work in the world was come again.

Yet even when he had rejoined Hilary in France, he dreamed of a cloistered life as well as a busy one; and he built at Ligugé a monastery, where he thought to seclude himself between his labours. It was vain for Martin to hope for a humble fate. He could not conceal the radiance of his face, or silence his silver tongue. His power to move the souls of his hearers was famous. It was known in all the cities of the province. Therefore one day, when the See of Tours fell vacant, and the dignitaries of the church discussed who should be the next Bishop, the people with one voice cried out for Martin.

The churchmen objected; the monk of Ligugé was too obscure, and far too young, to be Bishop of Tours. Such an honour was beyond a man of one-and-thirty years. But the people had set their hearts on him, although they knew that Martin himself would be still harder to persuade than the Princes of the Church. There never was a man who loved honours less. They met secretly to devise how to have him for theirs, and laying their heads together, made a plot.

On the day the election of the Bishop fell due Martin was praying in his cell in Ligugé, when a message came that Ruricius wished to see him. Ruricius was a citizen of Tours, already known to Martin, who came out to him at once. "What brings you from Tours, my son?"

"Father," said Ruricius, his eyes on the ground, "my wife is very ill. She prays you to come and comfort her."

This sort of prayer Martin was never deaf to; he instantly left the monastery with Ruricius, not knowing he was leaving it for ever. The two men set out on the road to Tours, and as they drew near the city Martin was aware of something strange happening behind him. Turning his head, he saw that the road was blocked by throngs of people, issuing from cover along the way. Every clump of trees was an ambush for the townsfolk of Tours. Men, women, and children were gathering in the rear, and if he had dreamed of going back to Ligugé, he would have had to press his way through an army of people. With each step he took forward, the concourse behind him grew denser. All Tours had turned out to waylay him.

"What does this mean?" asked Martin in amazement.

"Father, forgive us!" implored Ruricius. "We of Tours desire you for our Bishop."

"And your wife is not sick?" Martin looked reproachfully at the man, and Ruricius cast his eyes on the ground again. If he had tried to answer, he would not have been heard. The people were clamouring lovingly on all sides: "We will have none but you to watch over us!" Hemming him in, and pressing him on, they brought the bewildered Martin into the city.

The Bishops assembled there from the neighbouring towns teemed with indignation when the simple priest, with rumpled hair and crumpled habit, was thrust upon them as the successor to the See. One of the Bishops, Defensor of Angers, cried out against the foolishness of the people; it was useless, their minds were made up, they would have only Martin. The Bishops had to bow to the will of the laymen, and Martin was consecrated in the cathedral. So great was the crowd at the ceremony that the lector could not reach his place to read out the lesson. One of the clergy opened a psalter at random, and read in the lector's stead the first words his eyes lighted on:

"Out of the mouths of babes and sucklings hast Thou ordained praise, that thou mightest still the enemy and the Defender."

A shout went up from the people. God himself was on their side and Martin's—and Defensor turned away, covered with confusion.

For the second time in his life, Martin was compelled to a post he had not desired. As a boy he was made a soldier against his will; as a man, against his will he was made a Bishop. But he did not shrink from the responsibilities laid upon him. He found the rustics of the country-side practising strange rites and worshipping strange objects; and he set about uprooting the old superstitions which barred their way to the understanding of Christ. Rough ground must be broken up before seed can be sown, and Martin went about with crowbar and torch, beating down and burning the heathen temples. Then he built churches where the temples had stood. In one outlandish place he found men under the dominion of a mighty pine-tree, which they gathered together to worship. Martin commanded the pine-tree to be hewed down. There was a great outcry among the half-savage rustics. They came about the Bishop in a riot, brandishing their cudgels.

"Peace, children!" said Martin. "If you think I am doing this tree a wrong, bind me and seat me in the line of its fall. Then hack it down, and let it avenge itself on me."

The rustics agreed to lay down their cudgels, and let the pine-tree crush him for itself; and they bound him with ropes, and sat him where the tree must fall on him. And when it was hewn, it fell the other way. Then Martin spoke to the astonished crowd, and nearly all of them came into the fold; for when men listened to him, they could not resist him. It was said of him by the friend that knew him best: "Nobody ever saw him angry or disturbed, lamenting or laughing. One and the same was he always, bearing in his face as it were a heavenly joy; he seemed beyond the nature of men, nothing showed on his countenance but Christ, nothing in his heart but piety, peace, and pity."

Martin was at his old task of exorcising the devil. Sometimes the devils he found were men and women in disguise. In the ancient pagan Rites of Spring it was the custom of the rustics to dress themselves up like deities and demons; and now, when Martin was stamping out their superstitions, the wildest spirits among them tormented him. They took to disturbing him in his very cell, rushing about the monastery in the garb of Venus or Jupiter or Mercury.

Nymphs and satyrs interrupted his prayers; a man in a black ox-skin rushed through the cloisters blowing on a horn; a woman in leaves like a dryad danced outside in the moonlight. Whether these visitations were those of imps or men, Martin treated them all as the works of the devil, whom he once met in person, said legend, on a journey to Rome.

He had set out for the Holy City afoot, like any poor monk on the road, for he could never be tempted to any show or display. He had not gone far when the Devil accosted him.

"Good day to you, Monk! But can I be mistaken? It is the Bishop of Tours!"

"You are not mistaken," said Martin to the Devil.

"Is it possible! A Bishop using no other carriage than his own two feet! Why, any beggar has as good a conveyance. What a poor Master you must serve, Who cannot provide His Princes with better means of travel."

"He can!" said Martin. Pointing at the Devil, he changed him on the spot into a mule, jumped on his back, and urged him into a canter with the sign of the Cross. The road to Rome was long and arduous, and the Devil began to be sorry for his jibes. Soon he was panting and sweating, but whenever he showed symptoms of slowing down, Martin again made the sign of the Cross over him. And the Devil had to canter perforce, till at last he owned himself beaten.

This was the sort of legend that grew up about Martin, when men were telling of his encounters with the true and the false.

In time Martin's work in the countryside, and the people who beset him in the city, exhausted him. He had never ceased longing for sanctuary in a quiet spot, and presently he made a retreat for himself at Marmoutier, on the banks of the Loire, the river that runs like honey over a bed of bright sand. Shut in by sandstone cliff and wooded thicket, Martin's forest cell was hard to find. Eighty monks became his disciples there; they made caves in the soft sandstone to sleep and pray in, they wore skins of leather, ate but once a day, avoided wine, and shared all things in common. They sat at Martin's feet, to learn of him. Among them one day appeared a young escaped slave, whose name was Patrick. He was to be as great a Saint as Martin.

Martin grew old. His fighting days were over. He clung more and more to his hermitage at Marmoutier. But any trouble or sorrow in Tours drew him back from the serenity of his thoughts. Avitianus, a rough and ruthless lord of that city, brought a chain of captives in one night, for death on the morrow. The lights of his feast were extinguished, his house was in darkness, and Avitianus lay in his bedchamber. He slept, but not for long. There were cries on his doorstep, cries that rent the night. He sent for his servants and bade them see who was there; but the servants, wakened unwillingly from sleep, swore that their master had heard the cries in his dreams. He sent them away, and turned to his pillow again; and again the pitiful cries disturbed the night. Then Avitianus rose, and went to the door himself, and on the step he saw a white-haired man lying. He wore a monk's habit, his face was tear-lined, and his thin hands were joined in supplication. Before he could speak, Avitianus leaned down, and raised the aged Martin in his arms.

"You need not say a word," said the rough lord gently. "Every man knows of Martin that he loves mercy. What you have come to ask I grant, while your prayer is unspoken. Every prisoner's life shall be spared to-morrow."

So strong was Martin's power to move men's hearts, when his own was moved by the sufferings of man.

Tired out at the end of his life, when he was nearly eighty years old, Martin longed for nothing so much as his last hermitage in heaven. He knew the end was near, and was ready to go. But his disciples, longing to keep him with them still, fell on their knees and wept, and begged him to ask God to prolong his life. Forgetful of himself, he sighed and prayed: "Lord, if I am still necessary to Thy people, I would not draw back from the work."

But God thought Martin ripe for heaven, and took him.

He closed his eyes at Candes, where the Loire joins her sister river the Vienne. His body was laid on a boat without oars or sails; and it floated upstream on the golden shallows to Tours. The trees on the banks burst into flower as it passed, and music was heard in the air.

In the beautiful city of Tours he had his shrine. There was preserved the most precious of Martin's relics, his own torn cloak, the cloak whose other half he had given the beggar at the gates of Amiens. France held no relic dearer. Her Kings rode into battle, with the torn cloak borne before them like a banner.

A RHYME FOR MARTINMAS

(November 11th)

Sunny Martinmas, you come
When the bees no longer hum
    In the heat,
    Or on sweet
    Summer borders hover.
Then it was so warm, so warm!
Then my lightly-mantled form,
    Bared and hot,
    Wanted not
    Any other cover.

Now it is so chill, so chill!
Hear your beggar, Martin, still!
    Be my stay
    As the grey
    Wintry time grows number.
What sweet charity is spun
When November's mantling sun
    Falls its fold
    On the cold
    In Saint Martin's Summer.

SAINT MARTIN

· SAINT DOROTHEA ·

THERE was to be a banquet one night in Cappadocia.

That same day Sapricius the Governor was holding trials in his court. Near him sat Theophilus, a young Prefect, who had come to listen to the questions put to those on trial, and to their answers. Knowing his love of amusement, Sapricius said: "Do not expect to be entertained, Theophilus. To-day I am trying Christians, and they will all say the same thing about this Christ of theirs, Who was born three hundred years ago, and for Whom they are ready to die."

Theophilus said: "Still, I will stay awhile to hear these questions and answers. I have nothing better to do till I join my friends at the feast."

One after another the Christians were brought before Sapricius and questioned. One after another they refused to deny their faith. One after another they were sentenced by Sapricius. Theophilus lounged on his seat and listened idly. It was not very amusing; as his friend had said, one Christian was much like another.

"Who next?" asked Sapricius.

He was told: "The Maiden Dorothea from Caesaria."

Into the court was brought a young girl so fair and innocent that Theophilus roused himself to look at her. It would be a pity, he thought, for this Christian to die.

The questions began. She answered each one simply, and her voice did not falter.

"Do you fear nothing?" Sapricius asked presently. "Neither pain nor death?"

"Why should I fear death?" answered Dorothea. "Death will bring me to Him Whom I love."

"Who is it you love?" demanded Sapricius.

Dorothea answered: "Christ the Son of God."

"Where is this Christ?"

"He is everywhere," said the girl in her clear voice. "In His divinity He is on earth, in His humanity He is in heaven. He waits for me in Paradise."

Then Theophilus leaned towards the girl and spoke. "Dorothea, earth itself is paradise! Think of its flowers. How can you bear to leave them?"

She smiled at him. "What is your name, young Prefect?"

"Theophilus."

"Listen, Theophilus. In Paradise, where the woods are always green, apples as yellow as gold shine in the leaves, and lilies white as silver bloom in the moss. In Paradise, bright springs bubble for ever, the grass on the hill never withers, and the rose on the plain never dies."

"Enough!" said the Governor. "Since Paradise is so beautiful, you shall go there to-day."

He pronounced the sentence, and signed to his officers. As they approached, Theophilus said to her lightly: "Young Spouse of Christ! send me some apples and roses from Paradise."

"I will, Theophilus," said Dorothea, and was led away.

Theophilus rose, and strolled into the streets, to prepare himself for the banquet with his friends. The merry-making lasted far into the night. They feasted, sang, and drank, growing more boisterous, and one and another told some tale of what he had done that day. When several had spoken, Theophilus laughed: "These things you have seen and heard are common things. Now I this day have had a miracle promised me!"

"What then, Theophilus? Where have you been today?"

"I was in the court, hearing the Christians tried. And one fair maid told me she was going to Paradise, and promised to send me fruit and flowers from heaven!"

A shout of laughter rang around the hall, but died on all lips as though cut off with a knife. Out of the air appeared an angelic child, and stood among them. In its hands the little angel bore three apples and three roses, the like of which had never been seen on earth. It held them out to Theophilus, saying to him: "Dorothea, who has just entered Paradise, sends you these." The Prefect took them, and the angel vanished.

Next morning Sapricius sat again in his court. And again, when certain Christians had been tried, he cried: "Who next?"

He was told: "Theophilus of Cappadocia."

The Governor saw his own friend brought before him.

"What jest is this, Theophilus?" he frowned.

"No jest, Sapricius," answered Theophilus.

"What do you come for then?"

Theophilus said: "I come to confess Christ, in Whom I believe, for Dorothea's sake."

And the Governor sentenced him to Paradise.

A RHYME FOR DOROTHEA

(February 6th)

Dorothea to Theophilus: "I send
Apples of heaven to my earthly friend,
And roses. If your eyes would see them twice,
Meet me, Theophilus, in Paradise."

· SAINT BRIDGET ·

INTO the hall of the King strode Dubtach his friend, full of temper. The King, a wise man, asked: "Well, Dubtach, what brings you from your lands to me to-day?"

The nobleman replied: "It is that daughter of mine, the one we call Bridget."

"They say she is beautiful."

"She is as beautiful as the dawn, and I will not have her in my house another day!"

"Why will you not, Dubtach?"

"Because if I keep her I shall soon have no house left! She gives everything away, everything! whether it is hers to give or not."

The King began to smile. "To whom does she give?"

"To beggars. She has only to see man, woman, or child holding out a hand at the door, and she puts into the hand whatever is nearest. It was always so! When she was small she gave away her cake, her doll, the shoes off her feet—and then she gave her sister's doll and her brother's shoes. Now she is grown she clears the board of food for anyone who is hungry, and tells him to keep the silver dish she has heaped it on. Or she snatches up a gold goblet and fills it with drink, and gives some thirsty wretch both drink and goblet! When she has no money or jewels of her own left, a tale of misery sends her running for anybody's money and jewels. She does not even ask. She simply gives! My doors are beset with beggars who know her ways. I cannot afford to keep my daughter any more. So I have brought her to you."

"What do you want me to do?" asked the King.

"I want you to buy her," said Dubtach.

"Where is the girl?"

"Sitting in my chariot without."

"Let us go and look at her," said the King.

They went to the door, and there in Dubtach's chariot sat the maiden, as beautiful as hearsay. She was calm and radiant as the summer sea. Her hair was like a field of corn, her eyes were as blue as flowers, and she had as little thought of herself as a meadow has.

It seemed to the King he might do worse than buy her. Before he could say so, Dubtach roared a question at his daughter: "Girl! where is the royal sword, my gift from the King?"

"Father," said Bridget, "while you were within, such a poor man came by. Your heart would have ached to see him. He was sick and starving. He could scarcely walk. His clothes were falling to pieces. He was in need. I gave him your sword."

"My sword to a beggar!"

"There was nothing else to give him," said Bridget simply.

Dubtach was dumb with wrath. The King stepped forward, and hiding another smile he said to Bridget: "You had no right, my child, to give away the royal sword."

"But he was hungry. He can change it into bread."

"Still, the sword was not yours to give."

The maiden, with a look of wonder, said: "Sir, if a beggar came and showed me his need, I would give away my father and my king."

The King, a wise man, decided not to buy her. He said to Dubtach: "The best thing you can do is to get her a husband."

"There's a young lord in our parts who pesters me for her," growled Dubtach, "but she will have none of him."

Then Bridget said: "I will not make my vow to a man. I will only make it to God."

"How old are you, child?"

"King, I am fourteen."

"Then you are too young to know what is best for you." Turning to his friend, the King said: "If any young man is willing to wed her, let him."

Dubtach mounted his chariot, and drove his daughter back the way they had come. As they drove, she pleaded with him: "Father, do not compel me to this. Let me go to Usny, where the Bishop is, and let me take the veil."

"It is your wedding-veil you must wear, you wilful girl," said Dubtach.

On reaching his house he sent a message to the young nobleman, and bade Bridget make ready to receive him. She went to her chamber, but not to adorn herself; she knelt and prayed God to take her beauty from her. "It stands between Thee and me, O Lord," said she, "therefore destroy it, that no man will look upon me."

Word was brought that her bridegroom was below. The young man, who thought of her beauty by day and dreamed of it by night, had ridden eagerly to greet her. What cared he about her charities? Let her only be the mistress of his house, and he was ready to lay all he had at her feet, to do with as she pleased. He could hardly wait for her to come to him.

But when she came, he started from her, dismayed. Her face was drawn, her hair had lost its lustre. Where were those two blue eyes he had loved to look on? She now had only one, the other was sealed and shrunken, and all her bloom was withered.

"Bridget, is it indeed yourself?" he faltered.

"Yes," she said, "and I pray you not to urge this marriage on. I will be for ever grateful if you do not."

It was he who was grateful now to be released. He went to Dubtach and told him that a blight had fallen on his daughter; and her father, when he looked upon the child, knew that no man would wish to have her in his house. So he let the young lord go away without her.

Then Bridget said: "Father, I must go to Usny. The holy Bishop Maccail will not turn me away." And Dubtach no longer denied her.

With three other young virgins, Bridget went to Usny, and knelt before the altar in the church. The Bishop received the profession of the maidens, and put white habits on them. No sooner was the ceremony ended than Bridget's beauty flowed back to her again. She bowed her head, and put her sweet lips to the dry foot of the altar, and the sap flowed back again to the seasoned wood, and it turned as green as a tree when Spring is come.

Then Bridget went out with her maidens, and journeyed a long way till she came to a place that pleased her. A mighty oak-tree spread its shade over a grassy plain, and in its shelter Bridget built her cell. Now she could live according to her heart, with none to scold if she gave her all away. It was not long before the people of those parts came to know of the fair young nun who lived under a tree and never denied a beggar; and they called it Kil-Dara, the Cell of the Oak.

"She gives you the bread out of her mouth with a smile of beauty," they said, "and it tastes the like of no other bread at all. There is none so pure as she is."

"How would there be? She was christened in new milk as soon as she saw the light, for a pitcher warm from the cow was spilled on her as she lay whimpering on the threshold."

"Was it on the threshold she was born? Small wonder she has the smile of joy on her face. Did not the Bard say, 'Happy is the child that is born neither in the house nor out of the house!' "

The name of her and the fame of her ran like a sweet breath of wind round Ireland, and not only beggars flocked to the Holy Oak, but many young maidens, all eager to live her life. One after another Bridget habited them in white like herself, till the green plain seemed peopled with a flock of angels. Soon there were so many that dwellings began to spring up in the neighbourhood of the oak; one was added to another till a city was formed, and they called it Kildare.

Not only holy women, but holy men also were drawn to Kildare, and before long Bridget had to divide her church into three parts, one for the sacred virgins, one for the monks, and one for the lay people. She prayed St. Conlaeth to come and be bishop of the city, and the monks' father; while she herself was Abbess, and the mother of them all. And of all those, too, who came from a distance to ask her advice, and attend the festivals of her church.

A peasant's family once came to such a festival from beyond the River Liffey, leaving their cattle and their farm unguarded. During that day a great to-do brought Bridget to the Convent gates, and she saw a herd of cows with garments tied to their horns coming at a gallop along the road. As soon as they saw her the cows lay down at the gates, and everybody assembled to look at them. Suddenly the peasant from over the river exclaimed: "God bless us! these cows are ours!"

"Are the clothes yours too?" asked Bridget.

SAINT BRIDGET

"I couldn't say whose they are," said the peasant, but his child cried pointing: "Maybe they belong to those men there, da!" And now a band of naked men was seen coming at a run along the same road. When they beheld the crowd they stopped abashed, but Bridget, seeing only men that needed to be clothed, called from the gates: "Are these your garments, poor fellows?"

"Yes," they said.

"How come they to be tied to the horns of the cows?"

"The Liffey was swollen and we had to swim, and thought our garments would come dry so. But the cows ran off and left us as you see, bad luck to them."

"The cows, however, were not yours at all," said Bridget. "It seems you stole them in their owners' absence."

"It does seem so," they agreed.

"Now was not that a very bad thing to do!" cried Bridget, her blue eyes shining reproaches on the men. "It is very wrong to take what is not yours. Did you never think of these poor ones you were robbing? And did you never think you had only to come and ask me for cows if you wanted them? Oh, you have not been good!" she said severely. Then she undid the garments from the cattle, and gave them to the thieves, and bade them clothe themselves and come in to be fed. And at the end of the day the peasants went home driving their cows before them, and all were satisfied.

Another time she heard of a poor man in trouble, for he had killed a wolf running free near the palace of the King, and brought it in, expecting a fee for its head. But the wolf was the King's own creature, as tame as a dog, so the King pronounced death on him, and cast him into prison. The tale was brought to Bridget, who sprang at once into her chariot and drove by the bogside to go and plead for the man. And over the bog a great wild beast came leaping, outracing her horses, and with a bound it seated itself beside her in the chariot. When Bridget saw that it was a noble wolf, "Heaven sent you surely!" said she, fondling his ear. The wolf put his chin on her shoulder, and when she alighted walked beside her into the King's presence.

"Is it yourself, Bridget?" said the King.

"It is," said she, "and King, you must spare the poor rustic in your prison, for no man ought to suffer for a mistake, and besides that I have brought you a grander wolf than the one that was killed unwittingly."

The King without more ado took the wolf in exchange for the man; and maybe he knew it was useless to argue with Bridget anyhow. All things were fain to give in to her, from the King on the earth to the sun in the sky.

For one day, sprinkled with an April shower, she came quickly into her cell, and flung her wet mantle over a sunbeam shining through her window-bars to the floor. In her haste she mistook it for a beam of wood, and the sunbeam was glad to bear the virgin's mantle, but she herself went about her duties and forgot it. So the mantle hung there till after the sun went down. Presently one of the nuns peeped into the cell to see what light was shining there; and the sunbeam meekly begged her to remind Bridget that he was waiting to follow his master. But not till she came and lifted the mantle off him did the ray retire into the night to find the sun.

To her the sunlight was the best of God's gifts to earth; she would sit in the twilight watching it depart from the sky while she talked with her maidens of the joys of paradise. One evening the blind girl Dara sat beside her, and as the sun went down they spoke of God's love which is inexhaustible, and when the sun rose again they were speaking still. It rose behind Wicklow mountains, and first the peaks were gold, and then the light spread down the face of the hills to the plain, and the leaves on the trees and the blades of the grass were gold with glittering dew. And Bridget sighed with bliss and then with grief, because blind Dara could not see what she saw. She breathed a prayer and touched the sightless eyes, and instantly Dara opened them, and saw. For a little while she looked on the world in silence; then she said softly: "Close my eyes again, mother! while my eyes behold the world, I cannot see God with my soul." Then Bridget breathed a second prayer, and earth's vision passed away from Dara's eyes.

Maybe Bridget thought of this, when the time was come for it to pass from hers. Maybe she thought of a vision she had had long ago, when she heard the old Saint Patrick preach a sermon, and while he preached she slept. He came to her afterwards, when she was awake, and gently rebuked her: "Bridget, why did you sleep when the Word of Christ was being spoken?"

"Forgive me, father," she said, "I was sent a dream."

"Tell me the dream," said Saint Patrick; and Bridget said:

"I saw, and behold the land was ploughed far and wide, and sowers went forth in white raiment and sowed good seed. And it sprang up a white and goodly harvest. Then came other ploughers and sowers in black, and they hacked and tore up and destroyed that beauteous harvest, and strewed tares far and wide. And I saw again, and behold, the island was full of sheep and swine and dogs and wolves, striving with one another and rending each other."

"Alas, my daughter!" said Patrick. "In the latter days will come false teachers, who shall lead away many, and the good harvest sprung from the Gospel-seed we have sown will be trodden under foot. And there shall be controversies in the faith, between the faithful and the bringers-in of false doctrine."

But this had not come to pass when Bridget died. All her life she had looked on a golden world, and she only gave up that vision to behold one brighter.

A RHYME FOR BRIDGET

(February 1st)

Saint Bridget she was beautiful
In feature and in deed,
And she would give the world away
To anyone in need.
It was enough for her to know
Of beggars at her door
That women starved, and babes were cold,
And ragged men were poor.

Saint Bridget gave the world away
And cut her golden hair,
To dwell beneath the Holy Oak
Men speak of as Kildare.
The stick she put her lips upon
Broke straightway into flower,
The sunbeam in her greenwood cell
Lingered beyond its hour.

Saint Bridget laid her beauty by
That earth might leave her be,
And God bestowed it twice on her
Till angels leaned to see.
"Look, look! there goes the loveliest one
In Ireland ever known,
Our Bride who gave the world away
And made all heaven her own."

• SAINT PATRICK •

MILCHO, a rich chief of Dalrhidia in County Antrim, stood bargaining on the shore with Nial Navigiallach, an Irish King who had come to that coast to trade. It was in the dawn of the Fifth Century, when the times were rough, and kings were pirates and raiders. The coasts of both Britain and Gaul had reason to fear the raids of Nial of the Nine Hostages. In his boats were many youths whom he had taken captive here and there, and one and another of these was hauled out by Nial's crew of Picts, for Milcho to consider. The rich man needed another slave, and he looked the boys over as a farmer does a horse or a cow in the market. He quarrelled with Nial about the price asked for each, and all the time he had his eye on a lad of sixteen, who sat in the boat with his hands tied together. Captive though he was, there was nothing cowed about him; he held his head up proudly, and Milcho thought he would make a likely slave. So presently, nodding carelessly towards the lad, he asked, "Are you selling that one?"

Nial said, "I might, if I got his price."

"What is he?" asked Milcho.

"One that we took in a raid off the Scottish coast."

"No, Nial," broke in one of his men, "it was in that raid off Wales— or would it be the one off Cumberland?"

"Neither," declared another, "we got that boy in Cornwall."

"You're wrong!" cried a third. "That's the one we took off a farm in Gaul."

While the Picts fell to quarreling about where the boy came from, Milcho said to Nial, "It's all one. What do you want for him, anyhow?" And the chief and the king began their haggling all over again.

Nial had the boy fetched out of the boat, and said to Milcho, "There's a tall one for you!"

"I've seen taller," said Milcho.

"Mark the breadth of his shoulders," said Nial.

"I've known broader," said Milcho.

"Feel the muscles on him!" boasted Nial.

Milcho did so, and said, "I've felt tougher."

The king ran him up, and the chief ran him down, and so at last the bargain was concluded, and Milcho led the boy away to be his slave on the Mountain of Sleamish.

On the way the chief put questions to the boy, about whom the Picts had made so much argument. "Where did they take you?" he asked.

"From my father's farm at Enon," said the boy.

"Where might that be?"

"On the river's edge."

"What river, boy?"

"The river under Bonavem, where my father is a deacon of the church," said the boy proudly.

"Oho! Perhaps you hoped to be one too."

The boy knew himself to be a little careless of his religion; he answered, "My father hoped so."

"And hasn't your father a name of his own?" asked Milcho.

"His name is Calpurnius. My mother is called Conchessa. She is a Frank's daughter, but my father has the blood of patricians in him."

"And what may *your* name be, my young patrician?"

"Succath," said he.

"Well then, Succath, put away hopes of being a deacon like your da, it was off a farm, not off a church, they took you, and you shall keep my pigs, O well-born one!"

"First thrall to Picts, then thrall to pigs," observed Succath. "It's a queer thing life is surely." He stooped to pluck a tiny emerald leaf off the earth. "There's good things growing in this land however," thought he—"and evil ones too!" thought he again, as a viper hissed at him and darted away.

Thus Succath came to Dalrhidia on Mount Sleamish, and when Milcho's people asked, "Where was he born?" the chief replied, "Some say here and some say there," and the boy's birthplace remained for ever a matter of doubt.

Seven years Succath kept his master's pigs, and they were seven years of misery to the slave. But this they did for him, they led his mind, which was no man's slave, to God. His father's faith grew green in him, green as the three-leaved shamrock by the brown bog where the swine rooted. His labours began early in the dawn; but eager to serve God as well as his master, Succath rose still earlier than he need, and forestalled the daylight with his prayers.

Those seven years meant much to the boy's life. In them he came to speak the Irish tongue so well that you would take him for an Irishman itself, and he grew to know so much of the hearts of the folk that an Irish heart might have beat in his own breast. Moreover, Succath was no meek young man, but had a noble temper of his own, which made him still more like a hot-blooded son of Erin. At the end of the seven years, when he was three-and-twenty years old, he was more Irish than any other thing, and had a deep love for the island, the people, and the three-leaved shamrock which made the land so green. But some things in it he hated: such as the poison-snakes, whose venom was a danger to life, and the Druid priests, whose magic was a danger to the soul. And he hated his own slavery, which rendered him powerless to become, as was now his dearest wish, a priest of God, when he might fight against evils such as these. Meanwhile he did what he could with fasting and with prayers.

And then one night he heard a voice in his sleep: "Thou fastest well, and shalt soon return to thy country." And again the voice called: "Behold a ship is ready for thee."

When he awoke, Succath knew the time was come for him to go, and he rose and went under the cover of the night. The coast was many miles away, but he travelled safe till he reached it, and there, by God's power, was the ship. She was making ready to set sail for France.

Succath hastened his steps, and asked for passage in her.

"Can you pay?" said the Merchant Master of the ship.

"Yes, when we reach Bonavem," answered Succath.

But the Merchant stared at his mean garb, and roughly bade him be off. Not knowing what to do next he turned towards a little hovel on the shore, where he might hide himself; and as he went he began to say a prayer. It was not even ended, and he had not reached the hut before he heard a sailor shouting, "Turn back! He is asking for you!"—and when Succath came to the ship again, the Merchant simply said, "We will take you on trust." And so the ship set sail with Succath in her, and after three days was brought to beach in Brittany.

It was far from Succath's farmstead, a journey of at least a month, but the merchant-seamen decided to make it with their poor Christian passenger, who would recompense them at the end of it. They had with them their wares with which they hoped to trade in cities or at rich houses on the way. But they found none of these. It was at all times a hard, wild, stony country, and now it was desolate; for the savage Franks had lately ravaged it, taking the cattle and ruining the crops. After many rough and weary days they found themselves as cast away on land as ever at sea, and in a lonely forest, where they stayed exhausted, the Merchant thought they must all die of hunger. In his despair he turned to Succath and cried, "Christian! Is your God so powerful? Pray for us, lest we starve!"

"Have faith," said Succath, and fell on his knees and prayed. Soon there was a mighty stir in the forest, and a herd of wild pigs came trampling down the underbrush. With a shout the famished sailors sprang to their feet; and that night the forest was full of the smoke of wood-fires, and the smell of roast meat. The travellers stayed two days recovering their strength, and before they went from that place the Merchant came to Succath with wild honey in his hands. "See what I have found in a hollow tree," he said. "Take your share as an offering, Christian, and God be thanked."

So, after many years, when the young man came to his own door again, and the merchants took leave of him, he knew they carried with them something of his faith.

But Succath found he could not rest at home. The need to become a priest urged him elsewhere, for all the pleas of his friends and family; and chance or heaven led his feet south to Tours, whose bishop was the venerable Saint Martin. Martin was very old, Succath was young, but the younger and the elder met in their love of God. When Succath

SAINT PATRICK

had spoken with the Saint in his green cabin on the banks of the Loire, where he lived still like a hermit, Martin said: "If you wish to be my disciple I will teach you all I can; and because you are of a well-born Roman strain, you shall be called, not Succath, but Patricius."

So Patricius, whom now we may at last call, in the Irish manner, Patrick, realized his wish and became a monk, dwelling in a sandstone cave by the river, as all Martin's disciples did. From a monk he was to become a priest, from a priest a bishop. While he was on the road, and still a young man, he had a dream one night in which he saw written the words: "THE VOICE OF THE IRISH." Then he heard sounds of voices crying from a thicket where people were lost in the dark: *We entreat thee, O holy boy, come and walk again in our midst!"* And Patrick awoke, moved to the depths of his soul.

But the time was not ripe till he was a man in his prime, when he heard that Pope Celestine thought of sending a mission to preach the Gospel in Ireland. Who was so fitted for that mission as Patrick the bishop, who as Succath the slave had learned to speak the tongue, and know the land, and love the people? So once again a boat bore Patrick to the emerald isle, even as one had borne him thirty years earlier; but this time he went with unbound hands, that carried a bishop's crozier into Ireland.

* * *

One April day the herdsmen of Lecale in County Down looked over the sea and saw a boat coming, full of strange men. Their coming meant one thing only to these simple fellows, and they took to their heels and ran to the great barn where Dichu, their chieftain, was busy. "Master, make ready!" they shouted, "for the marauders are upon us again!"

Dichu came out of his barn, and called to his servants to arm and follow him; and he hastened down to the waterside, with his shield on his arm and his spear in his hand. But when he saw the boatful of men on the shore he was puzzled, for they were unarmed, and their leader smiled peaceably upon him.

"Who are you, strangers?" asked Dichu.

The leader answered him in his own tongue. "My name is Patrick, and once I was a slave in this land, yet in my soul I was more free than you who live under the shadow of the Druids. And now I am come to make you as free as I was."

"Step up to my house, Padruic, and tell me more," said Dichu. He signed to his followers to lower their spears, and brought Patrick and his monks into his hall, and made them welcome. When they had eaten, he bade the bishop speak, and Patrick stood up and said such things as had never before been said or heard in Erse. He had God's light in his heart, and God's gift on his tongue, and his eloquence was like fire that catches everywhere, and his reason like the tides that are according to heaven. Dichu had but to listen and believe, and he demanded instant baptism. But what then? There was no church handy, indeed, there was as yet none in all Ireland.

"Come into your own barn, Dichu," said the Saint, "and be baptized on your own threshing-floor."

And then and there divine worship was celebrated, among the tools and the grain, and Dichu and his servants were made Christians. Sab-hall-Padruic, or Patrick's Barn, they called it ever after. Soon the whole place round about became known as Saul, out of the name of the barn, and it became Saint Patrick's favourite resting-place, after his long journeys here and there. Many journeys he made about the land, and now he was listened to, now driven away. Now he converted multitudes like the stones on the shore, now one or two only, like precious pebbles picked up in this place or that. It is no easy thing to change the faith of a people, or to lift from them a power that has lain on them for many hundred years. Fear of the Druids was the power over that land. Among those who would not listen was Milcho, in search of whom Patrick had gone on foot. His old master would not even see the Saint who once had kept his swine; and perhaps this time it was not fear of the Druids that was in it. But swiftly and slowly, and always steadily, Patrick's word was weakening the sway of the Irish magicians, and they themselves were growing aware of it.

Everywhere that men and women gathered in knots, miraculous tales were whispered from ear to ear.

"Have you heard? This Patrick has given back to blind Sheila the sight of her eyes!"

"Have you heard? When Sean was lying dead upon his bed, this Patrick came and raised him to life again!"

"Have you heard? He preached one cold morning on a mountain-top, and the limbs of his listeners froze, and they had neither food nor fuel to warm them. This Patrick set them all to heaping snowballs, and breathed upon the heap, and that white heap of ice became a red-hot fire!"

"And have you heard how Lochu the Magus challenged him to a trial of magic, and Lochu spread his hands and rose up in the air half-way to the sky, but this Patrick only folded his and said a prayer, and a white arm reached out of a cloud and flung a snowball at Lochu, and he tumbled down head foremost at Patrick's feet!"

"And this have you heard, how Patrick built a hut of green wood and dry, and he challenged a Magus to sit in the green half wearing a monk's robe, and in the dry half he sate the Monk in the robe of the Magus, and then he set fire to the hut. And it was the green wood that burned, and the Magus with it, yet the holy habit was not even singed; and the dry timber would not catch, and the Monk had not so much as a blister, though the evil robe was shrivelled off him by the heat!"

"*Have you heard*" this and that wonder ran like wildfire from place to place, and each new tale of Patrick spelled the Druids' down-fall. Till at last men were telling the tale of the great encounter that finished them entirely.

The Saint had offered them his blessing, but they would have none of it, and held by their magic obstinate as mules, though Patrick told them, "Your magic is the curse of the country."

"Beware lest it be a curse on yourself," said they.

"On me, is it? Let *you* beware!" cried he. "If it comes to cursing, there's none can do it better than a bishop when he's roused. Yet I'd rather give you my blessing."

But when the Druids still sought to overthrow him with their spells, even the holy Patrick knew they were past his prayers. So he raised his hands over their fields, saying sternly: "I set my curse on you!" The Druids' crops and pastures turned immediately into bogs, and they saw their chief means of living vanish under their eyes.

"Will you let me bless you now?" asked Patrick.

"We can eat fish," they said. And they sat on the river-banks with rod and line, and filled their creels, and went on playing their tricks.

Then Patrick raised his hands over their rivers, crying again: "I set my curse on you!" The rivers ceased to have fish in them on the spot.

"Now shall I bless you?" asked Patrick.

"You shall not!" roared the Druids, and ran to their homes and put their kettles on. Heaven knows what dark spells they meant to brew over their fires, to destroy the holy terror they were no match for. But the Saint pursued them to their very hearths, and raising his hands over their kettles cried: "I set my curse on you!" And the kettles stopped boiling at once.

The Druids piled brushwood in armfuls on the red-hot peat, in vain. The wood flamed, the peat glowed, and the kettles stayed cold.

"Will you be blessed *now?*" said Patrick.

"We will not!" said they.

Then the Saint gave them up for a bad job. The land must be rid of its evils, and nothing was so evil in the land as they. He raised his hands for the fourth time, and pronounced his curse on their heads; and the earth opened under their feet and swallowed them up.

But the reptiles remained.

There never was a land so full of snakes. The reptiles he had hated in his slavery had multiplied out of all count, and now the tale went that this Patrick had sworn to rid Erin's soil of their poison, as he had rid her soul of the Druids' venom. A task indeed for any ordinary man! How would he set about it? *Have you heard?* He has made a vow: "I'll drum them out of the country!"

So he made himself a drum, and cut two stout sticks, and flourished them on his march across the land, drumming till his arms ached. Serpents, snakes, and scorpions fled before him! You never heard such drumming, or saw such flourishes! But his holy fervour nearly destroyed him entirely, for he struck the drum one such mighty blow that he knocked a hole through it. When next he struck, the virtue had gone out of the sound, and who knows what those millions of reptiles might not have done to him if an angel had not flown down out of heaven and patched up the hole? From that out, Patrick drummed more carefully, till the last little snake was driven into the sea; and then he blessed the land, so that they could never come back. Since then there has not been a snake or a Druid in Ireland.

It is one thing to destroy, it is another to build. If the land was cleared of the body of evil, superstition lingered on like its ghost. Patrick knew he had his chief work to do; he must teach the simple people of the country, and harder than that, the wise men of the cities.

Easter, the Christians' holy festival, was also a time of festival for the pagans, when they observed the Rites of Spring, and celebrated the sun's return to power. In the Temple of Temora on the Hill of Tara, King Leogaire and many princes and sages would assemble, and there would be gatherings on every height. Some days earlier all fires would be extinguished, as a symbol of the dark before the spring; and on a certain night the sacred fire in the Temple would be re-kindled, a symbol that spring-fire had come back to the earth. Then the gatherings would flock to re-light their own fires from the sacred flame.

That Easter-Eve the twilight was thronged with watchers on the hills, waiting to see the tongue of fire on Tara, where the greatest crowd of all surrounded the King. The spring dusk showed no sign of light on earth, though heaven had begun to light her stars. The mystery and the revelation were near.

Suddenly there were murmurs of fear and dismay.

"Look yonder! yonder! there's a red spark shining."

"Where?"

"On the plains of Shane! There is fire on the earth, too soon!"

"Some one has broken our ritual!" cried the King.

"Sacrilege! sacrilege!" cried the angry crowd.

"O King!" said one of the wise men who was present, "this fire if it is not put out will vanquish ours."

The King leapt to horse, and galloped away towards Shane, followed by the sages with the peasants at their heels. Among them stumbled little Herc, a child. They reached the place where Patrick was with his monks, tending the fire which he had dared to light. Leogaire seated himself, and bade those with him do the same—"And let none rise," he commanded, "when the law-breaker stands before me."

Then Patrick was brought into Leogaire's presence. He looked so tall and noble in his bishop's robes that little Herc stood up and said, "A blessing on you!" That child became the Bishop of Shane one day. The Saint smiled on the child, but the King frowned on the Saint as he asked roughly why Patrick had broken the law of his gods.

"I have not broken the law of my God," said Patrick. "This fire is holy fire, the Pascal fire."

"We know not that fire," said the King, "and my sages say it is dangerous."

"Let me argue that with your sages," offered Patrick. "Let me come to Tara to-morrow in the morning, and tell you all the meaning of this fire." And so it was agreed.

On Easter Day Patrick went up to the Temple, and all were assembled to hear him dispute with the wise men. They questioned him on the doctrines of his faith, and Patrick silenced their questions with the eloquence of his answers. He had wanted nothing more than this chance to make Ireland hear the Doctrine of the Trinity. It would have been a hard thing for another to make plain to the clouded minds of the pagan princes and sages, but what did Patrick do? He stooped down and plucked a little emerald plant out of the ground, the three-leaved shamrock grown in their own soil, and he said:

"This plant, that you know as well as you know the thoughts in your head, see how its three joined leaves spring from a single stem. If this has never seemed strange to you, let me now tell you something just as natural." And keeping the three-leaved shamrock for a symbol, he spoke to them of the Triple Personality of God.

Many converts were made that Easter morning. Dubtach the Bard sprang up and cried, "From this day I vow my gift of song to your Christ!" And Conall, a brother of the King, was baptized. And although Leogaire himself was not, he was so far pleased that he gave Patrick leave to preach the Word of God wherever he would.

He preached it everywhere. In County Meath the chiefs gave him their sons to teach, and he left behind him a colony of Christians that flourished like the shamrock. In County Leitrim he destroyed the Crom-Cruach, the crooked monument where the Druids had sacrificed to the sun. In County Connaught he was found by the daughters of King Leogaire, chanting God's praise beside their father's fountain. Ethnea the Fair and Fethlima the Ruddy had come down to the fountain to bathe. Full of awe, they questioned the white-robed singer, and by sunrise had accepted all he told them, and were baptized in the water of the fountain. In Sligo and Roscommon he built churches; Lent he spent praying on Croagh Aigle in Mayo. In Firawley he baptized seven princes and twelve hundred peasants. In Wicklow Prince Deichin would have none of him, but the poor herd Killan slew his one cow to feed him. In Munster, where he baptized Aengus the Chief, he set by chance his crozier on Aengus's great toe. The toe was pierced, but Aengus thought, "This must just be a part of it," and never let a sound. He supposed the flowing of blood was to do with the rites, and Patrick did not know the thing he had done, till those standing round began to murmur: "Behold the Struth-fhuil, behold the Stream of Blood!" Struill they call the place to this very day.

More sad is the tale of the devout and simple Colmar, who during a great heat toiled in the harvest-field from morning to night. Such a thirst was on him that he could hardly endure it, yet because he had heard that Patrick had forbidden the drink before Vespers, he would not sip water. That was not the drink Patrick had in mind at all, but Colmar mistook his meaning, and laboured, ached, and thirsted all the day, and as the bell let fall cool drops of sound on the evening air, Colmar with a sigh lay down and died.

"There lies Colmar Stadhach, Colmar the Thirsty," said his fellows. And maybe after that St. Patrick made it plain that when he spoke of the drink he meant poteen. We may believe water his favorite drink, so many are the wells named after him; some say he drank poteen too, now and then, some even say he was the first one to distill it. What will they not say!

At the end of twenty years the Saint saw his work in Ireland nearly completed. For his See he chose a hill in County Armagh, a beautiful site. But when he asked the owner for it, this man, whose name was Daeri, answered, "No, I want the hill myself, you can have a bit in the valley." Patrick went meekly away. Then Daeri felt out with himself, and looked about for a present for the bishop. He found a huge cauldron, holding three firkins, and his churls carried it behind him to the place where Patrick was.

"There!" said Daeri. "This cauldron is for you anyhow."

"*Gratias agam!*" said the Saint, for sometimes he forgot and said thanks in Latin instead of in Erse.

Daeri scratched his head, and went home muttering, "Gratzacham! what's Gratzacham? Only a fool would say Gratzacham for a cauldron the like of that. Gratzacham indeed!" By the time he reached his door, he was so vexed that he shouted, "Churls! go fetch my cauldron back again!"

The churls went, and returned with the cauldron.

"What did he say?" asked Daeri.

"He said Gratzacham again."

"Gratzacham when I give! Gratzacham when I take!" Daeri burst out laughing. "If he's a fool, he's a good-natured one! For that Gratzacham he shall have both the cauldron and the hill." And he ran to Patrick himself to tell him so.

When Patrick went to view the site for his cathedral he found a roe on the hill-top, suckling her fawn. The Saint carried the fawn on his shoulders to a quiet spot, and the roe trotted beside him; when they were happily together again, Patrick returned to the hill, and marked the roe's warm bed as the place for his altar. There, at the first synod held in Armagh, he celebrated Mass.

SAINT HUBERT

And now, having done so much for his dear Ireland, he turned his thoughts on Scotland over the water. His feet followed his thoughts, and that journey left the trail of his name on Britain. There's Kilpatrick in Dumbartonshire, and Crag-phadrig in Inverness. He had a church in Kirkpatrick, and from Portpatrick he took boat for Westmoreland, where the dale he preached in men called Patterdale; even as in Wales they named where he walked Sarn-badrig, or Patrick's Causeway. The sea has swallowed up Sarn-badrig now, it is a shoal in Carnarvon Bay that ships steer clear of. Patricks and Patters, Badrigs and Phadrigs, he strewed his name over rocks and churches, islands and valleys, causeways and cells, as a running stag scatters his scent. You could trace the Saint's journey across Britain by the names he left behind him in three tongues.

But it was in Ireland, long time after, that he died, in Ireland where he had baptized twelve thousand souls with his own hand, and built as many churches as there are days in a year; in Ireland, where he had served as a slave in his youth, as a saint in his age, he closed his eyes at last when his work was done. He was one hundred and twenty years old, they say.

"Have you heard? Our Bishop was taken ill in Sabhall-Padruic, and thought it would be fitting to die in Armagh, so weak as he was he set out. And on the way a blessed angel came down out of heaven and turned him back to Saul, the place he loved best."

It was on the Seventeenth day of March that Patrick died. Since nobody quite knew when and where he was born, that day became his feast, Ireland his country, and the three-leaved emerald shamrock his own emblem, worn throughout Erin on St. Patrick's Day.

A RHYME FOR PATRICK

(March 17th)

A bonnie bairn, my Patrick, the day that he was born!
    (Said the proud Scotch Thistle,
    In her purple and her bristle.)
A lusty babe, my Patrick, when I bore him one fair morn!
    (Said the Rose on her mettle,
    With her thorn and velvet petal.)
Ach! my child wass quick an' cleffer as a changeling-child whateffer!
    (Said the strong boastful Leek,
    Who was never very meek.)
Bel et bon toujours, mon enfant, mon amour!
    (Said the Fleur-de-Lis of France,
    That white flag on a lance.)

    But the wee triple Shamrock,
      The emerald-green vine,
    Said: "Let who chooses claim him,
    'Twas left to me to name him,
    His heart sleeps in Erin
      Wherever I twine,
    And by One, Two, and Three
      This Holy One is mine."

· SAINT HUBERT ·

OUNT HUBERT of Aquitaine leapt out of bed at dawn one day
in spring. The bright air of Easter blew through his window,
bearing the scent of the forest and the wild things that ran in
it. Hubert loved one thing only better than hunting, and that
was his young wife Floriban. When Duke Bertrand his father should
come to die, Hubert and Floriban would be Lord and Lady of Aquitaine; till then, they dwelled together in the court of King Pepin, where
Hubert had been brought up as a boy. He had been sent there for safety,
to be out of reach of the quarrels that troubled his father's Duchy. Even
King Pepin had his quarrels with the Duchies in his realm, but there
was greater safety in the shadow of a king than of a duke. Bertrand of
Aquitaine knew this when he sent his child into the king's care.

No thought of trouble lay on Count Hubert to-day. He was young,
he was loved by the King, he was heir to Aquitaine, it was spring, his
wife was beautiful, and outside his window, mile upon mile, stretched
the great deer-forest of the Ardennes. Hubert snatched up his hunting-
horn, wound it joyously, and began to dress himself with vigour.

Floriban lifted her sleepy head from the pillows. "Where are you
going so early, my dear lord?"

"To hunt, my darling lady."

Floriban raised herself on her white elbow. "To-day, my lord?"

"Why not to-day, my lady?"

"It is Good Friday," answered Floriban.

Hubert threw back his head and laughed at her. "Do the stags in
Ardennes know it is Good Friday?" He looked something like a gallant stag himself, she thought, as she answered gently: "But we are
men, not wild beasts, dearest lord, and we do know it."

He strode to the bed and took her face in his hands. "Keep the good
day in your way, sweet. I keep it in mine. Pray in the chapel, while I
go hunt." With that he kissed her, buckled his belt, and went.

He was not the only man astir in Pepin's court. Many of his gay
comrades had heard his horn, and made haste to join the Count when

he rode forth. He was the most passionate lover of the chase among them, and where he led they followed. It was a loud and laughing company that galloped over the plain to the dense forest. Hoarse shouts of men, deep baying of hounds, clear calls from horns, and the heavy thud of hooves on the rough turf, shattered the holy day. At the verge of the sunlit grass rose a dark thick wall of trees. The hunt plunged in, with Hubert in the van. He did not dream in how different a mood he would ride out of the shadow of those trees.

A stag broke cover, and the hunt was up. Horses and hounds, excited, went to work. The clamour of shouts and laughter was in Hubert's rear; he joined in it over his shoulder. Ahead of him, wings scattered in the branches, and furry feet scudded over the moss. Now and again a long-haired man of the woods peered out of a bush and crouched till the hunt had passed. The human denizens of the Ardennes were nearly as wild as the beasts who had their lairs there. Hubert cast them a scornful glance, and thought: "They'd be fair game, if ever stags were wanting."

And now he neither looked nor listened behind. His own hounds ran before him, thrusting through thickets, splashing over streams, and Hubert splashed and scrambled after them. The quarry was seldom in sight, but he could trust his hounds' noses. How long he had been riding with eyes, and ears, and every sense set forward, he could not have said, but presently he knew he was riding alone. Silence surrounded him. No more the shouts of his friends disturbed the air, there was no sound of hound, or horse, or horn; no savage eyes gleamed in the underbrush, and no wing shook the branches overhead. Nothing scuttled or flew, neither fur nor feather. Hubert was lost to man and beast in the heart of the forest.

It did not trouble him. Many a time before he had lost his fellows, killed his stag alone, and borne the antlers homeward for a trophy. But to-day there was something strange in the region he rode in. Its paths were unknown to him. He broke into a lonely valley, strewn with grey rocks, and plain to the eye at last beheld his quarry. It was the mightiest stag he had ever seen. It moved without haste or fear among

· 64 ·

the crags. Hubert's horse moved quietly after it, and ever his hounds ran silent, nose to earth—and stopped. For the stag had stopped, and turned to face the hunter. It stood as still as a tree. And lo! between the branches of its horns a Cross stood up, and on the Cross hung the Figure of Jesus Christ.

The Figure spoke: "Hubert, turn to the Lord."

The hounds lay down, their heads between their paws, the horse bowed its head, and Hubert in awe dismounted. He knelt, and clasping his hands, prayed to the Figure on the Crucifix.

"What is Thy Will? Tell me what I must do."

The Figure spoke again: "Go to my servant Lambert. What thou must do thou shalt learn of him."

The holy stag vanished, and was seen no more.

Hubert remounted his horse, and turned its head. The hunt for him was over.

When he rejoined his comrades they plied him with questions. Had the stag confused its scent and escaped him? Had it turned at bay? Had he counted its points, of what year was it? Was it a hart royal?

Hubert rode home to Floriban without answering. All the way, the Voice rang in his ears: "Go to my servant Lambert." It was a command, he knew, he must one day obey. But life was so sweet, Floriban was so fair, they were so happy. He could not leave her to go in search of Lambert.

For three years he and she held their delight. Then a son was born to them, and Floriban died. Hubert planted her name anew in her child, and called it Floribert.

But his heart was broken. Even the baby that almost bore her name could not mend it; and in his sorrow Hubert heard the echo of the Voice: "Go to my servant Lambert. What thou must do thou shalt learn of him."

Hubert went to the King, and laid at his feet the baldric and collar which were the badges of a soldier's service.

"I wish to resign these things to you, my lord."

King Pepin said kindly: "We know your sweet lady's death has stricken you down, but you are too young, Count Hubert, not to rise from a blow when life has dealt you one.”

“I do not doubt it,” said Hubert, “but I must rise to a new way of life.”

“True,” said Pepin, “for a great duty is soon to be laid upon you.”

“What manner of duty, my lord?”

“Death strikes twice,” said the King. “Your brother Eude sends word that Duke Bertrand, your father, is lying sick in Guienne. When you are the Duke of Aquitaine, you will need your collar and baldric, I think.”

“I think not, my lord,” said Hubert. He left his soldier’s badges with King Pepin, and took only his baby with him to Aquitaine.

The old Duke Bertrand lived to dandle his grandson, and closed his eyes in content. He asked no more than to be succeeded by such a son as Hubert, such a grandson as Floribert. But when his father had breathed his last, Hubert turned to his younger brother Eude, who had been watching with him by the bed.

“Brother,” he said, “I do not desire worldly honours for myself or for my child. I abandon the claims of both of us to the Duchy. It is you who must be Duke of Aquitaine; only, I charge you to support the King in his quarrels, as I would.”

“And what will you do?” asked Eude.

“I shall go to Tongern, to learn what I must do of Bishop Lambert.” And so at last Hubert obeyed the word he had heard spoken between the horns of the stag, and went to God’s servant Lambert. Placing himself and Floribert at the Bishop of Tongern’s feet, he told his tale, and ended: “Dispose of us as you will.”

Lambert thought awhile. Then, “Hubert,” he said, “when men who have lived in the world give up the world, their first and hardest task is to give up themselves. You shall conquer yourself in the place you have most enjoyed. Go back to the forest of Ardennes, and live there, not as a hunter, but as a hermit. After ten years you will be ready to make a pilgrimage to Rome.”

Having blessed Hubert, he took the tiny Floribert in his arms, promising to care for him; and Hubert returned to the heart of the wild forest where holiness had been revealed to him. Here, while the ten years passed over his head, he lived a life of self-denial, mastering the things that had given him joy in the world, and finding a joy beyond them. He heard the hunting-horns in the thickets, and had no wish to follow. He saw the lords gallop by in their gilded trappings, and was contented with his girdle of hemp. He met the wild men flying from the rout that scorned them, even as he had once done; and no longer saw them as savages to be spurned, but souls to be saved. And when a panting hart crossed Hubert's path, his desire now was to shield and not to slay it. The deer of Ardennes were sacred to him, for the sake of the stag that carried Christ on its antlers.

When the ten years were run, he set out for Rome, wondering how Pope Sergius would receive him.

* * *

An angel came to Pope Sergius in a dream, bearing in his hands a pastoral staff.

"Behold the staff of Lambert, Bishop of Tongern," said the Angel. "Lambert has become a holy martyr, and the See of Tongern is vacant. To-morrow in the Basilica of Saint Peter thou shalt find the man thou must ordain in Lambert's place." The Angel of his dream described a man to the Pope, and Sergius awoke. In his hands he found the pastoral staff of Tongern.

That day he went, as bidden, to Saint Peter's, and saw the man the Angel had described. He was kneeling at prayer in a shabby hermit's gown, with the dust of a long road on his sandalled feet. When the Pope asked his name, he answered: "Hubert of Aquitaine."

Pope Sergius put the pastoral staff in his hand, saying: "This staff was Lambert's of Tongern, who is no more. It is the will of heaven that you should be consecrated to his See. Come."

Scarcely was the ceremony begun when the Angel reappeared. He bore in his arms Lambert's pontifical habits, which were henceforth to be Hubert's. One thing only was wanting, the stole, which he had dropped while flying from Tongern to Rome.

The Blessed Virgin looked down from her seat in heaven, and took a stole that had been woven on the looms of paradise. It was of pure white silk, fringed with balls of gold, and embroidered by her own hands with silver thread. This she sent down to Hubert, and he stood fully robed, as no Bishop ever had been robed before. Moreover, when Hubert, having been ordained, was saying his first Mass, St. Peter appeared and gave him a golden key. By this sign Hubert knew that heaven had bestowed on him some of Saint Peter's power to bind and to loose.

With these special favours, Hubert returned to Tongern as its Bishop.

It was near the end of the Eighth Century. The Merovingian Kings ruled in France and Belgic Gaul, but their rule was beset with quarrels and dissensions. Pepin was dead, and Charles his son was dead; now Charles Martel, father of Charlemagne, the last and greatest of the Merovingians, was grappling with the troubles of France and Belgium. The Dukes of Neustria, Louvain, and Austrasia were at loggerheads. Some were for the crown, some were against it; and all were greedy for greater power and estates. But Charles Martel had one strong and firm supporter on whom he could rely: Eude, Duke of Aquitaine. Eude had not forgotten Hubert's command when he gave up the Dukedom to become a monk. The monk was now a Bishop with power of his own.

The brothers came together, the Duke and the Bishop.

"Brother," said Eude, "Charles Martel needs all the aid we can bring to him. While you were yet a hermit, you could do nothing; but now you are Bishop of Tongern, you can do much."

So Hubert, with his mind on heaven's affairs, found himself caught again in the affairs of men, and supported the King by all the means he had. And Charles Martel made him a still more powerful ally by endowing the See of Tongern with great estates, till at last it was the richest in the realm, and the town of Tongern was too modest to be its centre.

Hubert transferred his bishopric to Liège, and made the safety and salvation of its citizens his care. Old Duke Bertrand would have

SAINT GILES

approved of his doings. He built a wall about the city, made prudent laws, appointed magistrates, and fixed the weights and measures for the people. In as sane a spirit, he ordered the affairs of the Church, and called a council to revise its canons. The countryside was strewn with vagrant monks and hedge-priests, who went about preaching on their own in town and village. They were loose ends, unattached to a monastery, and some of them were of doubtful honesty, furthering their own welfare more than heaven's. Hubert found that the religious practice of the cities was disturbed by the floating population of monks; so he endowed Liège with a monastery, and ordained that confession should be made only to the known priests of the parish.

And then—he went once more a-hunting in the Ardennes.

But not the deer and the boar, his quarry was the souls of the dwellers in his own beloved forest, the wild men, who had never heard of Christ. They were scattered through the woods, and hard to find, but Hubert had never hunted stag, doe, and fawn as keenly as he hunted man, woman, and child through the wooded ridges and valleys. And they, who had cowered at the sound of the hunting-horn, crept out of cover to listen to Hubert's voice, not knowing it was a hunting-horn of another kind. One here, one there, they came to understand him, till at last he turned the forest into the mightiest of cathedrals, where Christ was praised and loved. And men called Hubert the Apostle of the Ardennes.

This was the longest and hardest task he set himself, but through it, and through all that followed it, he had the joy of his son Floribert at his side. The boy became a man in his prime, and Hubert grew old. Floribert was two-and-forty years, and Hubert one-and-seventy, when a new church was built in Brabant, and the aged Bishop journeyed to consecrate it. The long way took his strength, and during the ceremony he shivered and burned. He knew that he was seized with a fever, but Hubert had conquered fiercer fevers in himself than this, and he finished the rites, while none suspected his sickness. When all was done he turned to his servants and said: " I pray you, take me to my house in Fure, where Floribert is." He knew he was failing, and wished above all things to re-join his son. First by boat, and then upon a horse, he went to Fure, supported by his servants. They arrived late in the night, and Floribert came to take his father to his couch, but weary as he was Hubert said: "First to the chapel." He knelt before the Figure on the Cross, and prayed, and kissed the altar; and then allowed his son to lay him on his bed.

But instead of sleeping he tossed upon his pillows, and spoke of strange shapes and sounds gathered about him. What things did Hubert see and hear in his fever? The sound of horns? The sight of flying manes? The movements, slow and swift, of hounds on the scent? Most surely he saw the running of a stag, that turned and stood, most surely he heard a Voice speak between its antlers: "Go to my servant Lambert, and learn of him what thou must do." And last of all: "Hubert! turn to the Lord."

Floribert, watching by his father's bed, heard him murmur a psalm.

At daybreak he opened his eyes, peaceful and sane. It was a Friday in May. Forty-five years ago, he had wakened at dawn on a Friday in spring, to go a-hunting. It was a day he had cause to remember the rest of his life, and he did not forget it now as he said to Floribert: "Cover my face with a napkin, my dearest son."

Floribert did so. The fine cloth moved, while Hubert murmured the creed. When he had breathed the words: "Thy will be done," the napkin fell and was still.

They buried him in the Cathedral in Liège.

But later on they bore him to the Ardennes, where, even as he had lived, the Saint slept sweetest.

A RHYME FOR HUBERT

(November 3rd)

Count Hubert hunted in Ardennes
The hart with hound and horn.
So swift he rode he lost his men
Among the Easter thorn.
The music made by horn and hound
Brought none to mend his loss
And share the solitude of sound
And scent he rode across.

Count Hubert chased the noblest stag
That ever drew a pack.
It ran as it would never flag
Along the thorny track.
Sudden, it turned and stood. The young
Count kneeled upon the moss,
For lo! between its antlers hung
The Christ upon the Cross.

The hounds no longer sang their chord,
The horse in silence stayed,
The Figure said, "Turn to the Lord!"
Count Hubert knelt and prayed.
The stag, on whom the holy day
Had shed a golden gloss,
Serenely turned and moved away
And vanished with the Cross.

Monk Hubert winds no hunting-horn
To wake the wide Ardennes,
He bears no spear as night and morn
He hunts the hearts of men.
With never hound to scent its ways,
Nor horse to stamp and toss,
Hubert pursues the hart whose bays
Bear Christ upon the Cross.

• SAINT GILES •

"WHERE is the holy Giles?" asked the people of Greece. No man knew. The gentle old man had gone from the land that bore him. The time had come when he longed to live alone with his thoughts of heaven. Men loved him too much; in Athens where he was born he could not escape them. He crossed the seas to a land where he would not be known.

But indeed, he was known of men wherever he went. "A saint has been among us," they said when he passed, and he sowed his way through France like flowers in spring. Till even King Childebert heard of him, and asked: "Where is this holy Giles?"

In the Forest of Nimes Giles found a little cave. Creepers hid it, trees guarded it, and he asked no more than to dwell in peace for ever in this retreat. He lay down and slept, and gave no thought to his sustenance.

When he awoke, a snow-white doe stood in the entrance of the cave. She did not start when he held out his hand, but gazed with unfrightened eyes on the old saint. Then she moved softly forward, and let him see that her udders were full. Morning and evening the white doe came to nourish Giles with her milk.

The season passed, grass grew long and leaves grew broad, bright summer flowers replaced the flowers of spring, nestlings began to fly, and cubs to gambol. Giles sat in a green world, and dreamed of heaven; and heaven seemed all about him. And still at dawn and dusk, his doe let down for him the sweetest milk man ever drank.

The season passed, grass grew sere at the roots, leaves began to yellow, and flowers to drop their petals. The nests were empty, and the cubs were grown. And still Giles sat and dreamed in a changing world. Through a gold world instead of a green one now, his doe came like an angel morning and night.

King Childebert said: "Let us go hunting in the Forest of Nimes."

Near midday the King cried: "See! a white doe!" Like a great lily

· 74 ·

the doe gleamed among the trees. The hunt crashed through, and the white doe fled before it.

Saint Giles sat dreaming in the front of his cave. His dream was like still water, reflecting heaven. The surface of his dream was broken by sounds. Men were near. Before he could retreat into his cave, his white doe flashed between the golden boughs, and lay panting at his feet. An arrow winged after her, and grazed her shoulder. And then the King of France came through the trees.

He saw a white old man, clasping a white doe tenderly to his heart, while he plucked the shaft from its shoulder. When Childebert's shadow fell across the glade, the man raised his head, and his eyes met those of the King.

The King of France took off his hunting-cap. "Father," he said, "are you the holy Giles?"

Giles bowed his head. The world had found him again. "Do you know what you have done, my doe?" he whispered, and gazed into her eyes instead of the King's. And in these liquid eyes he saw that his doe had been the instrument of God.

He heard the King say with great reverence: "Forgive me, Saint, if I have hurt your friend. I cannot grieve, since she has led me to you. Come out of your hermitage and teach us heaven, for the world needs you more than this wood does."

Then the Saint arose and went away with the King. He also was an instrument of God.

"Where is the holy Giles?" asked the birds of the forest.

No creature knew. Only the white doe could have told them. But she, like the Saint, had gone, and was seen no more.

A RHYME FOR GILES

(September 1st)

Underneath the leaves of Nimes
Giles sat in a golden dream.

Night and morning, to and fro,
Came to him a milk-white doe.

The old Athenian questioned not
Who had led her to his spot,

Why she came, or where she went,
But knew that she was heaven-sent.

*

Underneath the leaves of Nimes
Giles beheld his white doe gleam,

Giles beheld the arrow wing
Sped by Childebert the King.

Then he heard the King's voice plead:
"Come, for you are he we need."

The old Athenian rose and went.
Giles was also heaven-sent.

• SAINT SIMEON STYLITES •

WHEN Simeon was a boy he kept his father's sheep in Syria. He loved the long days spent alone in the pastures. The bleating of the sheep and the barking of his dog did not trouble his thought, but the voices of men disturbed it like stones thrown into a pond. What lay under the pond he himself did not know. His thought had no word of its own, but because of it he was never lonely in the silence and the solitude among his sheep.

From the pastures he could see a distant mountain; at its foot lay a monastery, whose Abbot was called Timothy. When Simeon's eyes had dwelled on the monastery at the mountain-foot, they travelled up the mountain-side to dwell on its peak.

At night when the sheep were safe in fold, he turned his feet towards Gesa, the village where he was born. As he approached his father's house, where his mother was lighting a wick floating in oil, he supposed he would die there, too. Until he was thirteen years old, Simeon knew of no other existence.

One day he woke to find the world smothered in snow. It lay thick and deep on the pastures. Simeon went through the snow to the sheep-fold, and saw the ewes warm and content in their straw, with their lambs snuggled against them. He brought them their feed and drink, and let them be. But he was left with an empty morning on his hands. What should he do with it?

Some of the people of Gesa were going into the church, where he seldom went. Idly he followed the villagers. This would do to fill an hour or so. If the sun came out, perhaps the snow on the pastures would melt, and he could be with his flock again. If not to-day, to-morrow. But Simeon was never to be with the flock again. He went into the church, sat near the door, and listened.

"Blessed are the mourners and the weepers. Enviable are the pure of heart. Great is their gain who keep the Beatitudes."

The words reached Simeon's ears for the first time, a message that he did not understand; yet they seemed to rise out of his own pool of thought, which until that moment had no words. He plucked the sleeve of a man kneeling beside him.

"What does that mean? What shall I gain if I keep the Beatitudes? How *can* I keep the Beatitudes?"

"By a life of self-sacrifice," said the man.

Simeon looked puzzled. The man stepped out into the light, and the boy followed him. And there the man began to speak of Christ and His Gospels, and suddenly something became as clear in Simeon as the sun in the sky. All that he was seemed to vanish into the light; it was the sacrifice of Simeon's self for ever.

He did not give a thought to what he did next. He turned away from the man and went out of Gesa, passing his father's house for the last time. He left the village behind him, and walking as though in a dream, passed over the snowy plain to the mountain-foot. At the monastery gates he laid himself down. He lay there five days and five nights.

A monk went to seek the Abbot Timothy. "Father, there is a boy outside the gate."

"What does he want?"

"We do not know. He lies with his face to the ground and does not speak. And he does not eat or drink."

"Why should he eat and drink?" asked Timothy.

"He has been lying there like that for five whole days," said the monk.

Timothy rose and went to the gate himself. There on the ground lay the boy, as the monk had said. The Abbot leaned over him and asked: "Whence do you come, my son?" The boy did not answer.

The Abbot asked again: "Who are your parents? What is your name?" And still there was no answer.

Then the Abbot asked: "Are you afflicted? Have you committed a sin?" And after a pause he added very gravely: "Or are you a slave fleeing from your master? If so, I must return you whence you came."

At this Simeon lifted his head, and his face was bathed with tears. "No, master, no! Do not send me away. I am no slave. My name is

SAINT SIMEON

Simeon. My parents live in Gesa. I long to live the life of self-sacrifice. I long to be a servant of the Lord. Let me come in, and do not send me away."

Timothy raised him up, and led him into the monastery, where the monks were gathered to see the strange boy who had lain five days at the gates. "My sons," said the Abbot, "I deliver to you this brother. Teach him our rule."

Four months Simeon stayed among them, learning the psalter by heart. At the end of that time, one of the monks sought Timothy again.

"Father, we have complaints."

"Against whom?"

"Against Simeon. We cannot draw water from the well."

"Why not?"

"He has taken the bucket-rope. We have had to drink the water in the deep tank, and now it is all used up."

"What has Simeon done with the rope?"

"He will not say. He says very little. And he eats less. That is our other complaint."

"It is not wrong of the boy to love moderation."

"Moderation, father! if it were no more than moderation! But it is starvation. He sits at food among us, but does not eat. He carries his meat and bread away from table."

"What does he do with it?"

"Gives it to the poor at the gates. We have watched and seen him."

"But that is charity," said the Abbot kindly.

"True, father, but Simeon does this charity six days out of seven."

"Do you tell me," said Timothy, "that this boy eats only one day in the week?"

"Yes, father. He fasts from Lord's Day to Lord's Day, and we do not like it, because none of us can abstain from food like him, and it is not fair."

Timothy went once more to question Simeon.

"My son, where is the rope of the brothers' well?"

Simeon did not reply.

"My son," said the Abbot again, "why do you give all your food away? The monastery feeds the poor at its gates, and the brothers within must also eat enough to live. I forbid you, Simeon, to starve yourself to death. It is making the brothers angry."

To all this, Simeon answered not a word.

Then Timothy himself grew angry with Simeon, and said to one of the brothers: "Strip him, my son."

They took off Simeon's habit, and round the boy's body they found the bucket-rope, bound so tightly that it hurt his flesh. Nobody else could have endured it.

Timothy frowned and said: "Simeon, you must not punish yourself with penances. It is not necessary." And he told the monks to unbind the rope, and put the boy to bed, and salve his body. In two days, one of the monks complained again.

"Father, that Simeon!"

"What has he done now?"

"He has disappeared."

For nearly a week they looked for him in vain. One day as the Abbot was passing the empty and deserted water-tank, a thought struck him. He descended into the tank, and there at the bottom lay Simeon. He was weak and worn, and said to Timothy: "Servant of God, I entreat you to leave me alone for one more hour, that I may render up my spirit to heaven."

"Servant of God," said the Abbot very sternly, "come back to the monastery, and be content to live reasonably as your brothers do."

But Simeon made no effort to move a finger, so the Abbot called for some to come and help him. They lifted Simeon out of the tank by force. This boy, who outdid them all in self-sacrifice, was a thorn in their flesh. And as for Simeon, he could not understand why they did not leave him alone. Why could he not live solitary as a monk, as once he had lived as a shepherd?

*   *   *

At the end of another year he resolved to live by himself. No place seemed so deserted as the mountain-side. Simeon climbed up to the

Telanassus below the peak, where he found a little hut which he made his own.

But even here there were scattered villages, and going from one to another men passed the hut. Many a time the curious peeped in at him, and presently one went to the Arch-Priest of the little villages, saying: "Father Blasus, there is a holy youth in that old hovel under the peak."

Soon after, Simeon found the opening in his hut darkened by a shadow, and heard the voice of Blasus saying: "Be welcome! But do not live in this mean hut, my son, come and live among us in the village."

"I prefer solitude," said Simeon, wondering where on earth he could be alone.

Blasus looked round the hut. "But you have no food!"

Simeon replied: "I want no food."

"What do you want?" asked the amazed Arch-Priest.

"I want you to close up the door of this hut with clay," said Simeon, "and leave me alone for forty days and nights."

"But then, son, you will die!"

"That cannot be helped."

"It can be helped!" said Blasus indignantly. "To die by one's own act is a very great sin. I will only consent to do what you desire, if you will agree to let me bring you food."

"Very well," said Simeon. "Bring me ten loaves of bread and a jar of water, and if I need sustenance it will be at hand."

Blasus went back to his village for bread and water, and the curious people carried them for him to Simeon, and helped to seal the strange boy's hut with clay. At the end of forty days they came again, and pulled away the clay. On the floor of the hut lay Simeon, too spent to speak to them. Near him lay the ten loaves and the jar of water. The jar was full. Not a crumb or a drop had been touched.

Blasus bent over him, and shook his head. He put a wet sponge to Simeon's lips, and gave him the Holy Eucharist; and the boy sat up and looked at the people about him. One of them offered him lettuce-leaves, another chicory, and Simeon slowly ate a little of both.

"Let there be no more of this folly," said Blasus. "You can only stay here if you will fast within reason."

Simeon bowed his head. For the next three years he remained in his mountain-hut, eating just enough for his needs. But still he was not alone as he longed to be. The villagers often wandered past the hut, some curious, some reverent, some to bring him green food. Their coming and going was a trouble to him. He did not want to speak with any man. At the end of three years he went to the peak of the mountain, on which he had gazed from the plain where he kept his father's sheep.

He set up a circle of stones on the mountain-top, and put himself inside it. "This ring of stones shall be my house," he said to himself. "I will never more go outside its boundary." Having made this vow, he took an iron chain he had brought with him, fastened one end of it to the biggest stone, and the other end round his ankle, and sat down in the middle of the circle. Here, on this desolate peak, without even a roof over his head, Simeon thought he could at last live the life of self-forgetfulness, without hindrance.

*　　*　　*

Now there were tribes of wild Arabs in Syria, who rode about the deserts and the hills, pitching their tents for a night, breaking camp, and riding away. These tribes were the despair of the Christian priests, who could not gather them together to be taught the word of God; and when they themselves rode out into the desert to find the Arabs, the fierce brown men would not listen, and threatened their lives. They despised the lives of the meek and gentle monks, and needed miracles to wonder at.

Soon after Simeon had taken to his life on the peak, the tribes began to mutter one to another about the wonder-man who sat chained to a rock inside a ring of stones. Some of the wanderers, crossing the peak, had seen him.

"He sits as still as a stone himself," they said, "and does not answer when we speak to him. He looks at the sun and the moon, and his lips move in prayer. He fears not pain, or death, or any hardship. He is a mighty man."

The legend of the chained man reached the city of Antioch. Meletius, the Bishop, rode forty miles with his train, to behold for himself. There, true enough, inside a circle of stones, sat a youth, long-haired and lean, with his eyes on the stars, and an iron chain on his ankle.

Simeon brought his gaze down from heaven with a sinking heart. Could he never get far enough away from men?

"My son," said Meletius, "I am the Bishop of Antioch. Tell me why you sit chained in this ring of stones?"

"Because I have made a vow never to leave it."

"Son," said Meletius, "if your vow is a true vow, what profits the chain? Do you fear that without it you will rise and go?"

"I will never go from this place until I die," said Simeon.

Meletius beckoned to a smith in his train. "Strike off the chain," he said. The smith obeyed, and Simeon submitted.

But now that his solitude had been discovered, it was no longer solitary. People came from Cicilia and Antioch to look at him, and the tribes of the desert made his peak their road. So Simeon built a pillar, nine feet high, and sat on the top of it to be out of their way. He sat night and day, saying his prayers, and the tale the tribes told of the wonder-man grew in wonder. More and more Arabs clustered each day at the foot of the pillar, till Simeon felt their numbers pressing upon him. He doubled the height of his pillar to eighteen feet; and the Arabs' wonder increased, and so did their numbers. Then even eighteen feet seemed too near to men, and Simeon heightened his pillar to sixty feet; and that at last was enough. None could reach him, they could only look at him. He was then no more than twenty-one years old.

His legend was borne like a wind across the desert. Men who had never seen him talked of him.

"There is a wonder-man on the mountain-top! He lives on a column of six-and-thirty cubits. The space he stands on is two cubits broad. A little railing around the top keeps him from falling off. He never lies

down, it is not broad enough. Sometimes, but very seldom, he leans
against the railing to rest a little. He wears only skins; his food is sent
up in a basket. Day and night without ceasing he prays to his God.
Sometimes he prays on his knees, but mostly he stands erect. Now he
spreads his two arms like a cross on the top of his column, now his
arms fall to his sides, and he is as a flame on a torch. He can be seen
from afar like a shining light. When we are leagues away, we see the
cross or the flame. Morning and evening he bows himself down to his
God, till his head touches his feet. He bows again and again."

"It is true," said another. "I myself stood below and counted the
wonder-man's bowings. Twelve hundred and forty times he bowed
without pause."

"The God of such a man must be the true God," breathed the Arabs
with awe; and the sons of Ishmael streamed in their hundreds and
thousands over the sand, to hear the man on the column speak of
his God.

And when he saw them pouring like rivers from all quarters, when
he saw men coming out of their camps and their cities, Persians,
Armenians, Arabs, to mingle in one great sea at the foot of his pillar,
Simeon knew at last what he had been destined for, why a solitary
lot had been the only one for him, why God had set a peak before his
eyes when he tended his flock, why snow had fallen and driven him
into the church, why a man in the porch had revealed to him the life
of self-sacrifice, why he had lain five days in a trance at the monastery-
gates, why he had set himself penances no other could bear. All these
things were to lead him to the top of his pillar, where he could be seen
of the tribes that paid no heed to the monks. The sight of his wasted
frame, which he had taught to bear all hardship and hunger: the sound
of his distant voice, praising his God: these things made the sons of
the desert kneel round the column, praying to be baptized. They came,
whole tribes at a time, two and three hundred strong; sometimes even
a thousand brown men together rode or ran up the mountain. They
brought with them the images of their gods, they dashed them to bits
on the stones at the base of the pillar, they stood up and shouted their

faith in Simeon's God, and denied the darkness of their ancestors.

And Simeon saw the desert bloom like a garden, with the souls of men that flowered when he spoke to them.

Thirty years he lived on the top of his column, and men called him Simeon Stylites, or Simeon of the Pillar. Where he lived, he died. Only then was he brought down to earth again, and buried with great pomp at Antioch.

A RHYME FOR SIMEON STYLITES

(January 25th)

Simeon lived
In heaven's eye
On the top of a pillar
Hard and high.

Men came round
To wonder at him
On the top of his pillar
Gaunt and grim.

They saw his form
Stand up in the air
Like a flame on his pillar
Bleak and bare.

They heard his voice
Like a falling star
From the top of his pillar
Faint and far.

When he died,
Being worn and old
On the top of his pillar
Clean and cold,

Up went his soul,
Down came his bone,
Leaving his pillar
Lank and lone.

• SAINT NICHOLAS •

Joy had come to a certain house in Patara. A mother lay smiling on her pillows, a new-born babe lay on the head-nurse's lap, while the household women clustered round to look at him.

There's a fine boy!" said the head-nurse proudly. "Nothing wanting to him but a name."

"What shall you call him, madam?" asked one of the women.

"His name will be Nicholas," said the mother.

"Well then, little Nicholas, come and have your first bath," said the head-nurse, and she laid the tiny baby in a basin. Cries of astonishment broke from all the women. The new-born child stood upright in the water, and clasping his hands lifted his eyes to heaven.

"Oh madam, look!"

"Do not touch him," said the mother. "It is a miracle."

For two hours the tiny Nicholas stood with his hands clasped in his ecstasy, while the amazed women knelt about the basin, and adored him. It would hardly have surprised them if he had opened his lips and spoken, so sensible were his looks, so wise his eyes. They handled him with awe, bathing and dressing him at last as one who already knew more of holiness than they did. How else, but by divine knowledge, could he tell when Friday was come? Yet that day, when his nurse laid the baby to her breast, he turned away his head and would not suck. Not till the sun went down, and those who had fasted all day sat at their meal, would Nicholas allow a drop to pass his lips—but then he made up vigorously for lost time.

"My little wonder!" cried the nurse, dandling him as is the way of nurses. But few nurses surely had dandled a wonder like this child, who observed the fast-days before his lips could pray, and saw heaven from his bath in the hour he was born.

Nicholas grew up loving all young things. His parents, rich people of Patara in Lycia, were able to give their child more than he needed of toys and sweetmeats, money in his purse, and rich food at table. Sometimes those who have too much cannot see the needs of those who have too little, as though their own gold weighed down their eyelids and kept them shut. But when, like Nicholas, they have tender hearts, they keep their eyes open, and see the difference between rich and poor. When his parents died, he found himself a young man with a fortune which he did not wish to spend on himself.

How then would he spend it?

His friends must have wondered. He did not squander it. There were no signs of extravagance about his house or his person, and what he did with his wealth remained a secret. It is a secret that shall be kept till the end of his story.

But this may be told at once: that Nicholas had no use for his own earthly treasures, and turned his thoughts on the treasure that is in heaven. The ecstasy he had been born in never left him, and be became a servant of God.

His longing then was to see the Holy Land with his own eyes, and he took boat from Lycia to Alexandria, from which great port he would journey to Jerusalem. During the voyage, such a tempest swept sea and sky that the sailors gave up hope. The captain shouted his orders through the storm, and the men did their best to obey, but the ship tossed and strained and seemed as though she must part. All the captain's seamanship was useless. Then in the midst of the tumult a lightning-flash showed Nicholas kneeling at prayer, and his eyes were raised to heaven as though the salt waves that soaked his garments were the scented waters of his first bath.

"We are past praying for, priest!" cried the captain roughly. "Better let me lash you to a mast."

But as he spoke, the wind died down to a sigh, the black sky turned blue, the boiling sea became a sheet of silk, and the lightning vanished in the light of the sun. The sailors shouted for joy, and Nicholas said: "Nothing is ever past praying for."

"Tell us your name, priest," said the wondering captain.

"Nicholas," answered he.

"Remember it, men!" said the captain to his crew, "and if ever we are as near to death again, let us invoke the name of Nicholas."

And sailors did so then, and for centuries after, when Nicholas had joined the ranks of the saints. Many a one who prayed for aid in a storm vowed that he had seen Saint Nicholas himself standing at the ship's helm, his eyes raised to heaven, protecting the vessel and her crew from harm. And on their voyages seamen whittled little ships, and rigged them out trim and proper; and coming safely home, they hung the ships up in the sea-port churches, as a thank-offering to Saint Nicholas, their patron.

And children, who had cause to love him as much as sailors had, took Saint Nicholas for their patron too. He had a way of coming to know the needs of the young. Their pleasures were his care; so too were their pains.

It happened once in Myra, when Nicholas had become Bishop of that city, that three boys wandered into a wood on the outskirts, and came at night to an inn. They knocked, and the Innkeeper came at once to the door. He beamed in a friendly way, and rubbed his hands. "Well, children, what may you be doing here? What do you want so late?"

"We have missed our way, Innkeeper. May we come in and sleep?"

"By all means, children, and you shall sleep without dreaming."

There is nothing to be said for this Innkeeper. He lived by robbing those who put up at his hostel. When the boys were asleep he searched their clothes, and pocketed what he found. It was not much, but the clothes themselves were worth something. And then he looked on the three boys and sighed: "They are as pink and tender as sucking-pigs! What a pity that they are not sucking-pigs! What delicious pickled pork those three would make."

No sooner thought than done. By morning the three little boys were lying in pickle in the salting-tub; and truly they slept without dreaming.

Not so the Bishop of Myra. Nicholas, lying abed in his great palace, had a dream which made him sit up in sorrow and wrath. He had seen in his vision everything that had happened, and could not rest until he had discovered if it was true. That day he wandered in the forest arrayed in his mitre and robes, and at nightfall he came to the inn, and knew it for the one he had seen in his dream. He knocked; and the Innkeeper opened, the man in the vision. He beamed on Nicholas, and rubbed his hands.

"Well, Bishop, here's an honour, to be sure! What can I do for your Worship?"

"I have missed my way in the forest, Innkeeper. Can I come in and sup?"

The Innkeeper bowed him in, and gave him a seat. "What does your Worship fancy? A slice of ham? a cut of beef? or veal?"

"None of these, Innkeeper," answered Nicholas. "I have a fancy for the pork in the pickle-tub over there."

The Innkeeper glanced uneasily at his guest.

"Well, what's the matter?" asked Saint Nicholas. "Is the pork not yet salted enough?"

The Innkeeper turned white.

"Perhaps," said the Saint, "you only put it in pickle last night?"

The Innkeeper shook in his shoes so hard that he fell on the ground with his face in his hands.

"Mercy! mercy!" he wailed. "I confess! Have mercy!"

"We'll see about that," said Saint Nicholas. He crossed the room, raised his eyes to heaven, and made the sign of the Cross over the tub. The scum on the brine shivered a little, and three little sleepy-heads rose and peeped over the brim.

"Oh!" yawned the first child, "how well I have slept!"

The second stretched his arms. "Me too, without dreaming!"

"*I* dreamed," said the third child, rubbing his eyes. "I dreamed I was in Paradise."

The Innkeeper on the ground beat his breast, and wept.

Was there anything to be said for the Innkeeper? Yes, after all. Nothing is ever past praying for. Saint Nicholas knelt down with the three little boys, and put up a prayer to heaven. And even the Innkeeper was pardoned his sins, and was the better for it. He never pickled his customers again.

No wonder the Day of St. Nicholas became the children's festival. But his protection of the three little pickles is not the whole why and wherefore of that. The time has come to give away his secret, and tell in what way he liked to spend his riches when he was a young man in Patara.

There was in that city a poor nobleman who had three young daughters, so beautiful that many a youth would have sought them in marriage—but alas! they had no dowries. And without a dowry no girl, however fair, could hope for marriage in those days. So poor was the father that he had not been able to lay by a single silver piece for his eldest daughter; so poor that the time came when he knew not how to feed his children any longer. He saw no way between letting them starve, or selling them in the market, one by one, as slaves to rich men; and his heart was full of woe for the fate in store for them. As for the young maidens, they knew why their father sighed and turned pale when he looked at them. They dared not speak of it to him, but among themselves they whispered the names of certain youths whom they loved, and must not think of.

One night the poor nobleman stood cooling his brow at his open window, thinking, as the moon sailed out of a cloud, that she was no fairer than his eldest daughter, whom to-morrow he must part with. By no other means could he save her from death, yet the means would shame both his honour and hers. While he leaned in his casement, blurring the moonlight with his tears, a heavy round object sailed into the room, and fell clinking and chinking at his feet. Stooping, the poor man picked up a plump moneybag, and he could hardly believe his eyes when he untied the string and a stream of gold pieces poured out. He counted it eagerly in little piles. He had not seen so much money for years. There was enough to dower one maiden handsomely, and he thanked heaven that now he could save his eldest daughter from shame. When morning broke he told her the glad news, and instead of going to the slave-market, the young thing ran joyously to

the bazaar, to buy a silken veil, a bangle, and sweetmeats. That evening the youth she had named came to her father's house, the sweetmeats were eaten, and the lovers were betrothed.

But after dark the nobleman's heart was sore for his second
daughter, who was as lovely as the starry sky he looked on through
his window. For to-morrow she must go to the slave-market, since
miracles surely do not happen twice. Yet this one did! He had scarcely
formed the thought when a second fat round moneybag flew like a ball
through the window, and it contained a dower of gold equal to that of
the first. The nobleman ran out of the house too late to catch sight
of the giver. Next day he told his second child to put off her sorrow,
and buy herself a silken veil like her sister's. She returned from the
bazaar with perfume as well, and a jar of fruits in syrup, and before
the day ended she also was betrothed to the youth she wished to wed.

When evening fell the father was less unhappy than before, for
what had happened twice might happen thrice; and this time he was
determined to discover the unknown purse-thrower, and thank him.
For he could not doubt that the good fortune of her sisters would fall
to his youngest daughter, who was as sweet as the flowers that scented
the night.

A little before the time was due, the nobleman stole forth and hid
himself in an angle of the house; and before long a cloaked figure crept
to the window, clutching in one hand a bursting money-bag. But as
he aimed it at the open casement, the father came out of hiding and
seized his cloak—and was amazed to see that it covered young Nicholas,
the richest man in Patara. The grateful father fell on his knees, and
kissed the hem of the cloak. "Nicholas, servant of God, why seek to hide
yourself?"

"It is the way I prefer," said Nicholas.

"But then, your generosity will never be known!"

"Why should it be?" Nicholas seemed distressed that the mystery
in which he had wrapped himself had been revealed, even to this one
man. "Promise me, friend," he said, "that you will tell nobody."

"At least I must tell my children."

"The children least of all," said Nicholas. "If I choose to make young things happy by giving them presents, that is my business."

"And you won't come in and let them thank you in person?"

"I would rather they did not see me," said Nicholas. "Pray keep me dark, good sir!"

The father promised. Next day the youngest girl went to the bazaar and bought a silken veil, a necklace, and almond cakes. And she too was betrothed by evenfall.

But secrets have a way of leaking out. No doubt the three happy girls hung round their father's neck, and teased him with questions.

"Who, father, who? Who gave me my purse of gold?"

"Who, father, who? Who gave me my silken veil?"

"Dear father, who? Who gave me my handsome husband?"

"Who gave us the sweets, the fruit, the scent, and the trinkets? Who? Who? Who?" they cried, like little owls. And perhaps at last, their indulgent father whispered:

"Well! if you promise not to say a word — —"

And no doubt they promised; and no doubt they told. No doubt all the girls and boys in Patara wondered whether Nicholas would come to them too one night with presents. No doubt, if their parents wished to surprise them, they hid sweetmeats in their slippers while they slept, and in the morning the children shouted to each other: "Oh look, look, look what Nicholas has brought me!" No doubt they took to leaving their shoes outside their doors, for the generous one who preferred not to be seen. No doubt, from Patara in Lycia long ago, the custom spread through Asia Minor, and crept over the border into Europe, and sailed oversea to distant continents.

And it reached the present time, when little shoes were changed for little stockings, because stockings hold quite twice as much as shoes, and one ought not to limit dear Saint Nicholas, who loves above all to be generous in secret.

A RHYME FOR NICHOLAS

(December 6th)

Nicholas, Saint of Children,
Loves to spend his wealth
On pretty toys for girls and boys,
Leaving them by stealth.
The wind in the chimney
Hears children call:
"Bring me this, Saint Nicholas!
Bring me that, Saint Nicholas!
    A silky scarf,
    A bag of sweets,
    A big gold ball!"

Nicholas, Saint of Sailors,
Children of the sea,
When their sails are torn by gales
Close at hand is he.
The wind in the rigging
Hears the sailors cry:
"Save us here, old Nicholas!
Save us there, good Nicholas!
    Saint of Sailors,
    Bring us safe
    Home, high and dry!"

SAINT NICHOLAS

· SAINT FRANCIS ·

The Treasure

Two monks met at a fountain outside a city, to make their mid-day meal: one tall and fair of form, one plain and small of stature. They were travelling between Italy and France, without food or money, trusting each day to bring them enough to eat. In the cities they begged their bread at the door, and found a spring of fresh water to drink at, while they ate what they had been given.

The fellow-travellers opened their bags, and spread the contents on a flat stone by the fountain. Masseo, the tall monk, had plenty of new bread to set out; Francis, the small monk, had only a few dry crusts. The city housewives had given the plain monk their worst, and the handsome monk their best. Even so, the feast consisted of nothing but bread, both fresh and stale; yet as Francis brought forth his meagre store, and saw Masseo bringing forth his plenty, his eyes shone, and he said:

"Oh, Brother Masseo, we are unworthy of so much treasure!"

"Father!" exclaimed Masseo. "How can you call this treasure? This is poverty. It cannot be a feast, when we must eat it without knife, plate, or porringer, without cloth or table, with no house over our heads and no servant to wait on us."

Then Francis, who was a Saint, replied: "I call that the greatest treasure which has been prepared, not by man, but by God. God has provided this charitable bread, this fine table of stone, and this clear fountain. Let us pray to God to make us love with all our hearts the holy treasure of poverty, which His own Son enjoyed."

And when they had prayed, it seemed to the strong monk that flames of love streamed from the weak one's mouth, who called his meal of bread and water a treasure.

Listen to the tale of this same Francis, who was in love with poverty, yet had been born to banquets, wealth, and luxury.

The Poor Men of Lyons

Peter Bernadone was a rich cloth-merchant of Assisi. He had a wife, called Pica, and a baby boy, small and delicate, called John. The baby, like many another, soon found a nickname that clung to him all his life.

Bernadone's business took him frequently from Italy to France, where the best cloth and silk was woven on the looms at Lyons. The merchant would return to Assisi with scraps of French on his tongue. "Madonna Pica!" he would shout, "here I am home again! Where's my little Frenchman?" And he would catch up his tiny baby, toss him, and cry: "Oho, Francesco mio!" Soon all the household caught the trick of calling the baby "Il Francesco," the Little Frenchman, and as Francesco, or, as we call it, Francis, he became known to everybody.

Then, having greeted his household, Bernadone would sit and tell tales of any curious thing he had seen and heard in France; and Francis, playing at his feet, heard without understanding, when such phrases as "The Poor Men of Lyons" fell on his ears.

"What are these Poor Men of Lyons, then?" asked Madonna Pica.

"They are a sort of miserable monk," said Bernadone. "They go about in pairs, preaching two by two; they wear tunics of wool, wooden sandals, and seem to be in love with poverty." Bernadone glanced round his rich room, as though poverty was the last thing he could love. "Yet would you believe it, Pica? When they stand and preach, the common people listen to them gladly. Each time I go into France, I find more and more of the crazy loons on the road. Thank heaven we have no Poor Men of Lyons in Assisi. Come here, my little Frenchman!"

Francis helped himself greedily from the handful of sweetmeats his father held out to him, and crammed his mouth with them, while "The Poor Men of Lyons" still rang in his ears.

The Two Dreams

Francis grew up having every luxury that money could buy. Bernadone was of good but not noble birth, and it pleased his vanity to see

his son mixing with the young noblemen of Assisi, and made welcome
in houses like that of Bernard of Quintavalle, a rich and learned lord
of the town. Francis remained slight and small in figure, but his father
saw to it that he dressed as fine as any, with jewelled rings and chains
and belts to wear. His purse was well filled, Quintavalle himself did
not sleep on a softer bed, and when he entertained his gay young
friends, the table was loaded with dainties and delicacies, and the merchant's gold dishes were filled with the sweetmeats which Francis loved.
He revelled in everything the world could offer him, and when his purse
was empty his father stuffed it full of ducats again. None of his comrades spent money more freely, or rode to war more sumptuously
equipped. For this boy of twenty loved battle as he loved pleasure,
and cantered gaily to fight the quarrel of Assisi when she went to war
with her sister-city Perugia. The Perugians took him prisoner, kept
him a twelvemonth, and then, the quarrel being over, let him go again;
and back to Assisi the young man rode merrily, in all his finery, to be
made much of by his parents and friends. One of the first he encoun-
tered in the city was an old and shabby soldier, fallen on hard times,
and out of fortune's favour.

But Francis knew him for a man of honour and courage, and the
rich young man looked at the poor old one as though, for the first time,
he was looking at himself. Here they were, two soldiers home from the
war. What did it matter that one had grey hairs and the other brown?
What difference did it make that one wore splendid, the other shabby
clothes? Francis said to himself: "This man is my brother."

It was like a great truth breaking over him. He ran to his poor
brother impulsively, stripped off his own fine arms and tunic, and
made the old man put them on himself. Then he returned home, full
of a new fervour. In the night he dreamed that he stood in a vast
armoury. The walls were hung with arms and flags and banners, and
every one of them bore the sign of the Cross.

"Francis! all these are for thee and for thy soldiers!" said a voice;
and he awoke, and pondered the meaning of the dream. What were
these weapons, and who were his soldiers?

A new quarrel rose, between Assisi and Apulia, and again young Francis rode away to fight; but before he reached the scene of the battle, he fell ill in Spoleto, and once again, in the dream of his fever, he heard a voice from heaven questioning him.

"Francis! whom does it profit most to follow, the master or the servant?"

"The master, Lord."

"Why then dost thou leave the master for the servant?"

"Lord," answered Francis, "what wouldst Thou have me do?"

"Return to thy country, and it will be told thee."

Francis awoke in the morning with a cool brow. He dressed himself, and turning his horse's head rode back to Assisi, wondering when and how the thing would be told him. And as he rode he gazed with new eyes at the beggars on the way, and his heart was stirred with love for people he had never noticed before.

The Ruined Church

In Assisi his rich young friends were waiting for him, but Francis joined their revels without zest. His love of pleasure faded in him, as his love of men flooded him like light. Wherever he looked, his love and his pity increased, and he spent his days in charity, nursing the sick, and giving to the poor. At night, if he went to some feast at Bernard of Quintavalle's, he left his friends singing and drinking at table, and leaned in a window, gazing at the stars.

"Look at Francesco the star-gazer!" laughed his comrades. "Ho, Francesco, what are you mooning about?"

"He is pining for a bride," jested another. "Is that it, Francesco? Do you see the face of your beautiful love in the heavens?"

"I see," said Francis, "a face of love in heaven more beautiful than anyone can imagine." And he left the feast amidst laughter.

He could not stay in Assisi, he knew not why. Something urged him to ride to St. Peter's in Rome. The steps of the great cathedral were crowded with beggars. Francis went up between the ragged throng, and entered the cold shadow of the Dome. There were many shrines with candles burning, and offerings laid before them. The offerings were poor, and Francis felt his purse weigh in his pouch. He emptied it impetuously at one of the shrines, and rushed outside to the beggars on the steps.

"Give me your clothes, brother, in exchange for mine!" he cried to the most squalid man among them. The astonished fellow gave up his dirty rags, and went away in the young gentleman's finery; and all that day the merchant's son of Assisi sat with the beggars on the steps of St. Peter's. Well-to-do citizens, passing up and down, pitied or scorned him, according to their natures; but Francis minded neither their scorn nor their pity. He had discovered poverty.

Home he went to Assisi, full of the life he longed to share with his Saviour. He had known plenty, now he would know want; luxury, and now simplicity; he had had the pleasure of possessions, now he would have the ecstasy of giving up. In the little ruined church of St. Damian, he knelt and prayed, and the Voice of his dreams spoke to him again.

"Francis, seest thou not that My church is in ruins? Go, and restore it for me."

"With good will, Lord!"

He thought the Voice spoke of little St. Damian. He had not yet had his vision of God's great church that has no walls or roof, whose altar stands erect in the souls of men; he only saw the ruined chapel he knelt in, and was urgent to re-build it at God's request. As to the means, had his father not always given him all he wanted? He sped impulsively to the merchant's house, pulled the best bales of silk out of the presses, and rode to Foligno, where he sold not only the fine merchandise, but the very horse he rode on.

A few hours later the Priest of St. Damian was accosted by a flushed and excited boy. "Father, are you he who ministers here?"

"Yes, my son."

"Then take this gold, and restore these holy ruins in the name of the Lord."

"But where did all this money come from, son?" asked the astounded Priest.

"I sold some of my father's goods to get it," said Francis simply.

"But, my dear son, the goods were not yours to sell."

Francis could not understand this, where the work of the Lord was in question. He urged the Priest: "Take it, take it, father!" and still the Priest refused him.

Angry and discouraged, Francis flung the money into a corner.

"Go home, and tell your father what you have done," said the Priest.

"I dare not," murmured Francis.

The puzzled Priest then said: "I will shelter you awhile in the presbytery, though I cannot receive the money." And he took Francis in, leaving the gold in the dust.

Francis Finds Poverty

Peter Bernadone's temper was hot when roused. He came home to find his cupboards rifled of his best silks, and his son, it seemed, flown. He could hardly believe his eyes, and he raised a storm in the town, crying out on his son for a thief. The populace were loud in their sympathy, and kind feeling for Francis went out like a candle-flame suddenly blown on. When the boy's refuge was discovered, Bernadone hastened to the place, with a crowd behind him; and Francis, who saw them coming from a window, fled down to the cellar. Overhead the wrathful merchant beat the door and shouted: "My son, and my gold! Give up my son and my gold!"

The Priest refused to give Francis up to the angry crowd; the crowd grew more excited; and for three days Francis crouched in the dark cellar, and reached the lowest point of fear and despair. Then fear and despair turned into courage and hope, and he came up, pale and worn, into the light, to meet his father's wrath.

It was winter, and Assisi was white with snow. As soon as he appeared, the townfolks hooted, and pelted him with stones and balls of ice. "Home with you!" cried his father, hot with shame, and with blows he drove his petted son through the streets. On reaching the house, he tied Francis up in his room, and locked the door.

But when the furious merchant was gone on some errand, Madonna Pica stole up to her son's door. She unlocked it, entered, wept over and caressed him. "Your father will forget his anger presently," she said.

"My Father," said Francis, "has no anger in His heart."

Madonna Pica did not understand. She thought she would find Francis cast down and broken; instead, she saw a new light in his face, and heard a new tone in his voice. Was this her delicate child, her "little Frenchman"? No, Pica did not understand. She undid his bonds. Francis stood up and gently bade her farewell.

"Are you running away from Assisi?" Pica asked.

"No, I am going back to St. Damian." And Francis returned to the little ruined church, which seemed to him the beginning of all his hopes.

Instead of going to haul him out again, Bernadone strode to the magistrate. "I come to accuse Francis Bernadone of theft! I appeal to the law to force him to make restitution." Officers of the court were sent to bring Francis before the raging merchant and the judge.

The judge asked: "What do you say to your father's accusation?"

"That I am now God's servant," answered Francis, "and am outside the civil law."

The judge advised Bernadone to appeal to the Bishop, and it was in the Bishop's Palace of Assisi, before a crowded gathering of citizens, that Francis met his father for the last time.

Purple with rage, the merchant stated his case, ending: "I demand the return of my gold, got by goods that he stole! I demand, moreover, that he shall renounce all claims on me and on my estate! I disown Francis Bernadone as my son!"

A murmur went round the assembly. Bernadone's violence was so great that it turned the tide of sympathy towards Francis again. The Bishop addressed him gravely.

"It is your duty to restore what is not yours."

Francis replied: "I have brought the money with me. Here it is. I give him back everything he ever gave me, even to these clothes." And with one of his excited impulses, Francis stripped off his clothes so that he stood almost naked before the people. He made a heap of the garments on the floor, and placing on the top the bag of gold—"Bear witness all present," he cried, "I have restored to Peter Bernadone everything that is his. Till now I have called him my father, I call him so no more. God alone is my Father from this hour."

The Bishop threw his own mantle round the young man, and tenderly embraced him. The merchant took up the garments and the gold, and left the palace with a bitter heart. A labourer's rough frock was found for Francis, and he went out of Assisi into the snowy woods, singing the praises of God.

The First Meal of Scraps

"Francis! seest thou not that My Church is in ruins? Go, and restore it for me."

"With good will, Lord."

These words he carried with him into the forest. But before he could build the Lord's House, Francis told himself that he must become worthy. No heart and hands were fit for the work that hankered for things of the world. So for awhile he wandered, teaching himself.

He taught himself to love the ache of winter as much as the ease of summer. He taught himself to prefer the scratch of his frock to the smooth feeling of silk on his tender body. He came to a monastery where he begged to work in the kitchen, and he who had been served by many servants became a cook's scullion. He worked his only garment into shreds, and then he wandered on to Gubbio, to beg another garment of a friend. He wandered everywhere, shirking no hardship, shrinking from no disease, nursing even the lepers, and kissing the hands of those whom no man would go near.

When he had taught himself to love poverty, he went back to Assisi, and set about mending the church of St. Damian.

One by one he carried big stones from the quarries on his own shoulders, and hewed and plastered them with his own hands. The townsfolk, who had first flattered and then despised him, now came to wonder at him as he worked. The rumour had soon flown round: "At last St. Damian is being restored! And do you know who is restoring it?

SAINT FRANCIS

None other than Francis Bernadone, though you would scarcely know him to look at him. His clothes are rough, his hands are rougher, his body looks as though it had never been fed. Yet the greatest change of all is in his face. He never looked so joyful in his life!"

The Priest of St. Damian brought him food as he worked. Francis, casting his eyes on it, asked: "What is this?"

"Your dinner, my son."

"But here is fine bread, and fish, and fruit, that you do not afford for yourself."

"My son, you were brought up softly, you cannot eat our poor fare."

"Father," cried Francis excitedly, "I can eat the poorest—I can eat whatever other men reject!"

He snatched up an empty bowl, and ran with it through Assisi, begging from door to door. The housewives filled his bowl with the broken bits from their table, the stale, or damaged, or discarded scraps. It was a meal he would once have shuddered at; but Francis brought it back to the ruined chapel, set it before him, and raised his hands above it. "This is the table of God," he said, and having blessed the poor food, he ate with a joyful heart. Then he said to the Priest: "Bring me no more meat. I now know how to provide for my bodily needs."

With those words, though he hardly knew it yet, he pronounced the first rule of the Order of St. Francis.

The Church of the Angels

St. Damian was restored and whole. The folk of Assisi aided in the work, and when Francis next turned to restore the Church of St. Peter, they aided that too. And still it seemed to Francis that he was not yet building the Church the Lord had intended.

At the foot of the hill on which Assisi perched lay the tiny church of St. Mary of the Angels. It stood in a place called the Little Inheritance. This church, the humblest Francis had yet found, was in bad repair, and so he set about his third rebuilding. When it was done he asked permission to live in the Little Inheritance, and use the Church of the Angels for his devotions. Permission was granted, and he made his home there. People began to ask: "What is he? Is he a monk? He lives the religious life, yet he is untonsured. Is he a monk or not, and what is his Order?"

Francis himself did not know. He only tended his faith in the garden of heaven, which had no flower like his. The flower broke into bloom one Sunday morning, in the year 1208. He was hearing Mass in his own little church, when revelation came to him in the words of the Gospel:

"Provide neither gold, nor silver, nor brass in your purses, nor scrip for your journey, neither two coats, neither shoes nor yet staves. And as ye go, preach, saying 'The Kingdom of Heaven is at hand.'"

Here at last, in these words, was all Francis had looked for. The words had touched his ears often before, as the sun may touch a tree before it blossoms. And then, one day, the same touch opens the flower. When the flower was revealed to him, Francis must have seen himself as a child, and heard his father say: "The Poor Men of Lyons —a sort of miserable monk, who wear woolen tunics and wooden sandals, and seem to be in love with poverty. They go about the roads, preaching two by two, and the common people listen to them gladly."

The Poor Men of Lyons!

That was the life! That was the Church the Lord required him to build. It was not with stones, that stand on one spot only, it was with words that go all over the earth. This Church he would build had no walls but the air, no roof but the sky. It was not here, or there, but everywhere.

Francis rose up and left the Church of the Angels, cast off his shoes and threw away his staff, and replaced his leather belt with a girdle of hemp. And so, without purse or scrip, he went out of the Little Inheritance on St. Barnabas Day, to preach the Gospel in the highways and byeways.

The First Four Brothers

"The Peace of God be with you."

This was his salutation to all he met; and having uttered it, he began to preach. It was a new wonder to the people of Assisi to hear Francis saying words that were like fire piercing the heart. He preached in the open air, like the Poor Men of Lyons, but not two by two, for he had no companion. Presently he found one.

Bernard of Quintavalle, the wise and wealthy lord, had seen with surprise the change in his young friend: how he had been despised by the townsfolk, abused by his people, and mocked at as mad, and how through all he had been as one deaf and dumb. For he did not answer, and seemed not to hear the abuse and contempt of his fellows.

Bernard thought: "The Grace of God must be on him," and wished to know more. One evening, when Francis was passing through the street, he called him in to sup, and after supper Bernard made him sleep in his own chamber. He himself lay pretending to sleep only, and watched what his friend did. When Francis heard Bernard snoring, he rose up and prayed all night, saying no other words than: "My God! my God!" But he said them with so much ecstasy, that his fervour passed into Bernard's heart and soul.

In the morning Bernard said to his friend: "Brother Francis, my heart is set on leaving the world, and following you."

"Let us first be certain," said Francis, "that what is right for me is right for you." And he made Bernard say the Mass with him, and then open the missal for a sign. It opened at the words of Christ to the Young Man: "If thou wilt be perfect, go and sell that thou hast, and give to the poor, and follow me."

Then Francis said: "Blessed be our Lord Jesus Christ;" and Bernard of Quintavalle went out and sold all he had, and gave his wealth away to widows and orphans, pilgrims and prisoners, hospitals and monasteries. And he became St. Francis's first companion, and they went together preaching two by two.

Within a week they had been joined by two others, Pietro di Catano, a churchman, and Egidio, a citizen of Assisi. These three, the Lord, the priest, and the burgher, went back to live with Francis in the Little Inheritance. One thing, however, puzzled the newcomers, and Egidio asked: "Brother, what Order of Monks are we?"

St. Francis answered: "Our Order will be like the Fisher, who puts his net into the waters and takes a great multitude of fishes, keeping the larger and leaving the smaller."

Egidio wondered at the answer. Their numbers were but four. Whence would the multitude come that Francis spoke of?

Two by two, the four went about and preached, and wherever they preached, people listened. Some called them maniacs, some called them messengers, but whether they praised or scorned them, still people listened. They could not ignore these four men who, in a greedy world, had chosen poverty. Some of the listeners went away disturbed, while others followed the preachers of their own free will, and came to live in the Little Inheritance. Before long, the house of Francis was overcrowded. And still the question remained without answer: "Who are we? What is our Order, and what is its Rule?"

St. Francis went forth in the night to ask God for guidance. "God be merciful to me a sinner," he prayed. His ecstasy came upon him as he prayed, and he heard a Voice say: "Be not downcast because ye are few. Behold the multitude of your Order on the way." In a vision, he saw men coming towards Assisi from every part of the earth: Frenchmen and Spaniards, Englishmen and Germans, all living the life of poverty with Christ, each in his own tongue inspiring the rest. Before the vision faded, the Rule of the Order of St. Francis was made clear to him.

In the Little Inheritance he called his followers round him, and told them his vision. "Brothers, listen now to the Rule of our Order. Our three great vows are Poverty, Chastity, and Obedience. And brothers, our Poverty must be absolute. Other orders of monks hold possessions in common; while they live in their cloisters preparing their own salvation, they have money to dispense, and food to eat. But we must have nothing except the food we shall eat, and the garment we shall wear, from day to day; and God will provide them. We must not store anything, or live in cloisters. Our first care must not be our own salvation. We must not desert the world, though we are not of it; we are God's heralds, and we must go about proclaiming His Kingdom. Our care must be for men, not for ourselves. This is the Rule of our Order."

Before the Order of the Franciscans could be founded, its Rule must be laid before the Bishop of Assisi. He had never considered one like it before; all other Orders of Monks had goods of some sort—how could they live without provisions in their larder and money to support the monastery? But Francis had no monastery to support; he had not even a larder. "You will have a terrible struggle," said the puzzled Bishop, "if you try to live in the world without possessions."

"If we had possessions," said Francis, "we should need arms to protect them."

"It is true," said the Bishop. The lords of the Umbrian cities were rapacious, ready to raid and rob on the slightest pretext. "Well, have your way," he said, "I agree to your Rule. It only remains for the Pope to confirm it."

The Three Orders of St. Francis

Pope Innocent walked on the terrace of the Lateran. The presence of a stranger in a poor brown habit disturbed his thoughts. He waved the man away, and went on meditating.

That night he dreamed of a great church falling down; as it tottered, two men ran forward to bear it on their shoulders. One of them was the Spanish St. Dominic, the other was the small plain man in brown who had approached the Pope on the terrace, and been turned away.

Next morning the Pope had the stranger brought to him, and Francis came, followed by a little band, all in brown habits. Francis explained that this was the dress of the Order he wished to found, and he told the Pope the Rule they meant to observe. The Pope was as surprised as the Bishop had been, and raised the same objections. Francis met each with those "words like fire that pierces the heart," and in the end Pope Innocent confirmed the Rule, and gave the new Order of Franciscans the tonsure.

There was joy in the little band. Blessed by the Pope, they set forth again for Assisi: shoeless and staveless, penniless and foodless, they proceeded by castles and cities, begging their way. Now in the market-place, now in the piazza, now at the gateway of some feudal palace, St. Francis poured his heart out. If the soldiers gibed, the lords and ladies listened, brought him into the hall, and asked him questions.

How could they themselves live the life of Christ? Could they not do so without becoming monks and nuns? They were moved—they believed—but they did not want to give up the world entirely. St. Francis remembered the multitudes in his vision. The world was full of people ready to follow him, as long as they could remain laymen and laywomen. All the world could not become monks and nuns, and those who lived in it needed a Rule to live by. He promised the lords and ladies a Rule they could follow, without renouncing the world, and instead of founding one Order, he founded Three.

The First Order of St. Francis was for the Brotherhood of the mendicant Friars called Franciscans. The Second Order was for the Sisterhood of Nuns, called the Poor Clares. The Third Order was for the laymen and laywomen, who were neither monks nor nuns. The Orders laid down the rule of life for each.

The Franciscans must take the vows of Chastity, Obedience, and Poverty. They must think only of bringing God's Kingdom to men, and never of themselves. They must not provide for their needs beyond the day.

The Poor Clares must take the same vows, but need not beg abroad for their daily food. The brothers did the begging for the sisters, while the sisters in their convent prayed for the brothers. The Sisterhood had been founded by St. Clara, the daughter of a nobleman of Assisi. When she was a beautiful girl of seventeen, she left her father's house to live according to the life of St. Francis. As he had been followed by his friends, she was followed by hers. She took counsel of St. Francis in her troubles, and he in his asked for the light of her prayers; and for her and her nuns he founded the Second Order.

The Third Order was less simple to think out, but at last St. Francis made the rule for its members who lived in the world. They must keep God's Commandments, bear no arms except for the Church or their country, use only such oaths as were necessary, enter no theatres, and attend no balls; and in their quarrels never go to law, but settle the trouble by conciliation. Four days in the week they must abstain from meat, and at each canonical hour say seven prayers.

The Three Orders grew, gathering more and more members every year; and many as were the Franciscans and Poor Clares, the Third Order outnumbered Friars and Nuns together. The Rule was followed by men and women all over the earth, from kings and queens to the humblest of their subjects. Rich men and poor were joined in one great bond throughout the world. The lay members gave to the Friars who preached on the road, the Friars followed their lay brothers to the grave, and the Poor Clares nursed and helped and prayed for them all.

The last and prettiest thing Francis did for his Rule was to bring in the beasts, whom he loved, and called his brothers. He asked the Pope's leave to make a Manger at Christmas in the Church, with the Ox and the Ass both present in the straw. At Grecia, near Assisi, in 1223, the first Christmas Crib was made, that the people might see for themselves the Night in Bethlehem. All night long, from crowded homes in the cities and little huts on the hills, the people thronged with candles and torches to Grecia, and stood round the Crib, singing carols with the Friars; and all night long St. Francis stood sighing with joy beside the Manger. His friend Giovanni saw in a vision a Child, waking and stretching its arms to St. Francis as he leaned down—and Giovanni thought: "He has wakened the sleeping Christ in the hearts of the people."

Life in the Little Inheritance

St. Francis's vision came true. First one man had caught his faith from him, then three, and from those four, others took fire, and from those still more, as they walked and preached through Italy and France—and then through Spain and Germany, and over the sea to

England. The Franciscans grew in their multitudes like rivers, and one and all were welcome at the Little Inheritance, although there was no monastery to house them.

Only a wall of mud enclosed the Church of the Angels, with rows of little thatched shelters down two of its sides. In the front wall was a gate which led to Assisi, standing among her cypresses on the hill; in the back wall was another gate to the forest, by which St. Francis stole forth to his contemplations. He had made a little cave in a thorny bush, where he sat and meditated all one Lent, taking no more than two small loaves with him, and eating but the half of one of them.

Yet he did not counsel others to do as he did, if by excessive fasting they hurt themselves. When he heard of a brother who fasted so that he could not sleep for hunger, Francis took bread to his cell, and sat and ate saying, "Share my supper, brother." Then, because Francis ate, the brother did likewise, giving way without shame to his hunger; and afterwards, Francis told his friends what had happened, and said: "Remember, there are due limits, even to fasting. It is our task to forget our bodies, but hunger makes us remember them as much as overeating. Therefore, when a brother treats himself too severely, do as I did, and persuade him to eat without shame."

"Do as little children do," was one of his directions to the brothers, when they were at a loss. There was even a child dwelling in the Little Inheritance, a boy so innocent that St. Francis admitted him to the Order, in spite of his youth. The child longed to do as Francis did in all things, and noticed that the Saint went out secretly to pray by night. One night the boy lay down to sleep near the Saint, and he tied the cords of their two gowns together, that Francis might not rise without waking him; but when he woke, the cords had been softly unknotted, and the Saint had gone. The child crept into the forest in search of him, and presently saw a marvellous light streaming out of a thicket, and heard voices that were not like the voices of men. He beheld St. Francis sitting in the light, speaking with Christ and His Mother, St. John and many angels. The vision overcame the little boy; and next he found himself being carried in St. Francis's arms, like a lamb in the arms of a shepherd. He wondered if St. Francis would scold him, but the Saint only said: "Brother, tell no man your vision as long as I live." Long afterwards, when the child was grown, he told what he had seen.

Francis called all things his brothers and sisters, children as well as monks and men and women: not only children, but the birds and the beasts: not only the birds and the beasts, but the sun and the moon: not only the sun and the moon, but life and death.

His human family had put him from them, but he had taken all men and all things for his family. And once it chanced, on a moonlight night in winter, that a brother heard a voice outside his shelter, and peeping out saw St. Francis making seven little figures in the snow.

"Here is your wife," he was saying to himself, "here are your four sons, and here your two servants. Care for them, or they will perish of cold. But if the care of so many trouble you, care for the Lord alone."

The brother saw tears rain down St. Francis's face as he turned again to his shelter, leaving his little snow family in the moonlight.

The Brothers and Sisters

Once when St. Francis was preaching in Alvia, his listeners were disturbed by the screaming of swallows. The Saint was standing on a rise in the ground, and to those below him seemed to be wreathed in birds, for the swallows flew round him as bees round lavender, and his words were drowned in their twittering. Francis said courteously: "My sisters, you have had your say, now let me have mine. Listen in silence to the word of God." The swallows settled about him like good children, and that summer day the Saint's congregation was made up of men and birds.

All things knew him for their brother, from the wild turtle-doves he saved from sale in the market, to the timid leveret given to him for food. The doves went to his bosom as into a nest, and the leveret took shelter in his gown. "O my innocent sisters," said he to the doves, "why have you allowed yourselves to be caught?" And "Come to me, little brother leveret. Why did you suffer yourself to be taken?" He let the leveret go free, and the doves fed from his hand. He could no more harm a creature than a child. On the Lake of Rieti a fisherman caught him a tench. "God bless you, Brother Fish," said the Saint, restoring the tench to the water; it swam in the boat's shadow, till the Saint gave it leave to go. In Osimo, a shepherd was driving a lamb to slaughter, and the Saint offered his brown robe for it, having nothing else. The shepherd refused, but a merchant who knew him came by, and gave the herd his price and the lamb to the Saint. With the lamb beside him, Francis preached in Osimo to the townspeople. He left the lamb, when he went in the care of a convent, and one day received from the nuns a robe, sheared and spun from the lamb's wool.

Even the savage creatures he called Brother. "Come hither, Brother Wolf," he called to a great fierce beast that was pestering the people of Agobio. "I command you in Christ's name to do no more harm to anyone." The Wolf lay down at the feet of the Saint, and Francis admonished him gently, saying that he knew it was only from hunger his Brother had killed the cattle, but if he would promise to live at peace with men, the folk of Agobio would feed him as long as he lived. The wolf wagged his tail as a sign that he gave the promise, and St. Francis led him into Agobio, and told the people of the pact saying: "Brother Wolf, pledge me your faith to the promise you made outside the gate." Then the wolf lifted up his right paw, and laid it in the hand of St. Francis, and the people of Agobio marvelled and praised God. Thereafter the wolf lived among them till he died, going from house to house like a good dog, and was fed by all for love of himself and the Saint.

And yet again, when he and his friends were on a lonely road, the Saint heard a flock of birds singing in a tree, and said: "I will preach to my little sisters"—and this was his sermon.

"My little sisters, the birds, much bounden are ye unto God, your Creator, and always in every place ought ye to praise Him, for that He hath given you liberty to fly about everywhere, and hath also given you double and triple raiment; moveover He preserved your seed in the ark of Noah, that your race might not perish out of the world; still more are ye beholden to Him for the element of the air which He hath appointed for you; beyond all this, ye sow not, neither do ye reap; and God feedeth you, and giveth you the streams and fountains for your drink; the mountains and the valleys for your refuge and the high trees whereon to make your nests; and because ye know not how to spin or sew, God clotheth you, you and your children; wherefore your Creator loveth you much, seeing that He hath bestowed on you so many benefits; and therefore, my little sisters, beware of the sin of ingratitude, and study always to give praises unto God."

While the Saint spoke, the birds spread their wings and bent their heads to the ground, and when he ended, he made the sign of the Cross over them. Then all the birds rose up in the air in the shape of the Cross, singing wondrously, and one part flew East, another West, another South, and another North, still singing.

The Feast from Perugia

Once, when St. Francis was in Rome, a Spanish Monk fell on his neck and said: "You are my comrade. Your work and mine are the same. If we stand by each other, nothing can prevail against us." The monk was St. Dominic, the second man who upheld the church in the dream of Pope Innocent.

Four·years after their first meeting, Dominic heard that Francis was holding a great meeting of his Order on the plain of the Church of the Angels outside Assisi; and the Spanish Saint journeyed to hear his Italian brother preach at Pentecost. From Assisi he looked down upon the plain, and beheld thousands of Franciscans assembled about the Little Inheritance. They sat in companies, here forty, there eighty, there a hundred together, praying and speaking so softly that the silence was scarcely broken, although the whole Order of brothers from all over the world was gathered there, at least five thousand strong. A Cardinal standing beside Dominic murmured: "Of a truth this is the camp and the army of the knights of God." All the brothers had crossed Europe without a crust to start with, and they had come to a place where there was not a crust to end with.

Dominic heard Francis preach to them, and marvelled to see the multitude prostrate itself in prayer, without a thought of provision. He wondered still more as he went about the plain, and saw that the only shelter prepared for the five thousand was willow trellises and mats of straw.

"How will all these be fed?" he asked himself. "Is not my brother rash to leave the provision to chance?"

But Francis, going about the trellises and laying down the straw coverts, was saying: "My children, we have promised great things to God, and been promised greater by Him. Let us observe our part, and He will His."

God's part had been done already. Hearing of the great assembly, the hearts of all the cities had been moved to send supplies to the five thousand Franciscans. Over the plain, from Perugia, from Spoleto, from Spallo, Fuligno, and Assisi came trains of horses and carts, laden with bread and wine, honeycombs, beans, and cheese, with pitchers, cups, and napkins to serve the friars. Dominic fell on his knees before his brother. "Truly," he cried, "God hath a special care for these holy poor, and I knew it not."

But Francis saw without wonder the feast of the Pentecost. He always knew that God would provide.

The Soldan

Now that his faith was flooding the Western world, Saint Francis set his heart and soul on the East. Choosing twelve of his brothers, as Christ chose his Apostles, he journeyed into Egypt to convert Melek-el-Khamed, the Soldan of Babylon.

The Christian hosts were struggling against the Saracens; Francis joined them, with the single aim of being captured. He allowed himself and his companions to be seized, and they were brought bound before Melek-el-Khamed. As soon as the Saint was in the Soldan's presence, he opened his lips and preached. So divine were his words, that the Saracen could not withstand them.

"Christian," he said, "I will spare your life and your comrades', if only you will stay awhile with me, and speak to me daily." Then he signed to a slave to bring gold and gifts to the Saint, thinking so poor a man must rejoice in them. Great was his wonder when Francis put them aside.

"If gifts do not please you," said the Soldan, "say what will please you most?"

"Leave for my brothers to preach throughout your kingdom," answered Francis.

The Soldan said: "It is granted. Further, I will teach them a sign, to keep them from harm as they go."

Then Francis sent forth his friends to preach two by two in the land of the Saracens, and he left them there like seed sown in barren soil, which they might make green with their words. But he himself must return to Italy, where the heart of his Order was.

Before he went he spoke once more with the Soldan, trying to win him to the Christian faith, but the Soldan said: "Brother Francis, I would gladly turn to Christ, but for that my people would slay both me and you, and we still have work to do before we die. But whatever you bid me do to be saved, I will."

"My lord," said St. Francis, "keep yourself free, and prepare yourself for God. In time, when I myself have gone to heaven, I will send two of my brothers to baptize you at the last."

Then the Saint and the Soldan took leave of each other on earth. But many years after, when he lay on his deathbed, the Soldan was told that two friars in brown robes were at the gates. "Bring them to me!" said the Soldan and when they came he looked on them with joy, saying: "God has sent me His servants, according to the promise of St. Francis." And before he died, he was baptized by them.

The Stigmata

When Francis was but three-and-forty, his sight and strength began to fail. He was too fragile for the hard life he had set himself; and even now he did not spare himself.

Between the Vale of Spoleto and Romagna, he came on a journey to the Castle of Montefeltro, where a festival was afoot. After his custom, he preached to the revellers, and greatly moved the heart of Orlando of Chiusi. This knight, desiring to do something for Francis who had done much for him, said: "Father, in Tuscany I have a beautiful lonely mountain, the Mount of Alvernia, which is a fitting place for solitude. Let me give my mountain to your Order, that whenever you wish you may go there into retreat."

"I accept your loving offer," said the Saint; and with Brothers Masseo, Leo, and Angelo, he journeyed to keep the fast of St. Michael on Alvernia. At the mountain-foot he rested under an oak, and a host of birds, flapping their wings and singing joyously, alighted on his head and arms and knees, and settled at his feet. By the joy of his little sisters the birds, Francis knew it pleased the Lord that he had come to Alvernia, and he ascended the mountain, and kept the fast with the three brothers who had come with him.

On Holy Cross Day, the Fourteenth of September, the Saint left his brothers sleeping, and prayed with his face to the East: "Oh my Lord Jesu Christ, grant me these two graces before I die, that I may feel in my soul and my body the love and the pain Thou too didst feel on earth."

When he had prayed, a Seraph with six flaming wings came down from heaven, and two wings sheltered his head, and two were stretched in flight, and two covered his body. The Mount of Alvernia burned with a shining light, and the Saint in his exaltation glowed with love and pain. When the vision had passed he looked down at his hands and feet, and saw that they bore the marks of the nails of the Cross. And he knew that Christ had bestowed on him the Stigmata, as a sign that Francis was His standard-bearer for ever.

On the journey back from Alvernia he was very still, and Brothers Masseo, Leo and Angelo knew that some wondrous thing had happened to him. When they had reached the Little Inheritance, they urged him to make known what it was, for the sake of the Order. Then Francis told them how the Lord had signed him with the miracle of the Cross, and how he knew he had but two more years to live.

The Death

In those two years, people said of him: "Of all his body he made a tongue." He was worn like a frail curtain, through which light streams. His bodily strength and sight were now quite gone, but the strength and sight of his spirit were greater than ever. When he was taken ill at Nursia, the people of Assisi came with a litter to fetch him home, that he might breathe his last in the Little Inheritance, the spot he loved best of all. Although he could not see it, he knew when they were near.

"See that ye never give up this place, my sons," he said. "Now set the litter down, with my face towards Assisi." They did so, and he blessed the town of his youth.

Once more in his own shelter, he asked for pen and ink, to write a letter to the Lady Giacoba of Settisole. "I pray you to send me a hair-cloth for my burial," he said—and added, like a child: "And I pray you to send me some of the little cakes of almond and honey, which you baked for me when I was ill in Rome."

As he laid down the pen, a brother entered. "Father, the Lady Giacoba is at the door. She comes from Settisole, bringing you a hair-cloth, and sweet cakes."

Soon after this, he called his brothers round him, to eat with him for the last time; and he gave them some last advice, ending with this: "I pray you, my brothers most dear, that ye love one another." Then he blessed them all, and said: "Welcome, Sister Death!"

His face grew bright and joyful beyond measure, and he lay without saying a word for two days more. Just after vespers a flock of crested larks rose in the evening, and wheeled around the hut where the Saint lay. He loved larks best of all his little sisters, their intent, he said, seemed ever towards the praise of God. The larks flew and sang like a little choir from heaven. When night fell they went with the light, and their brother Francis went with them.

A RHYME FOR FRANCIS

(October 4th)

The kinsmen of Francis
Were not as another's.
The birds were his sisters,
The beasts were his brothers.
These were his names
For the great and the small—
Was not God Father
Of him, and of all?

The night and the morning,
The water, the wind,
The star and the daisy,
Were each of his kind.
God was the Father
Of him and all others,
And flowers were his sisters,
And trees were his brothers.

"Brother, good morrow!"
He said to Friar Sun.
"Sister, good even!"
To Moon the sweet Nun.
"God is our Father,
We know of no other,
And Death is my sister,
And Life is my brother."